Members'
favourites

Over 70 inspiring recipe ideas from
Weight Watchers Leaders and Members

SIMON &
SCHUSTER
ILLUSTRATED

London · New York · Sydney · Toronto · New Delhi

A CBS COMPANY

First published in Great Britain by
Simon & Schuster UK Ltd, 2012
A CBS COMPANY

13 5 7 9 10 8 6 4 2

Simon & Schuster UK Ltd, 1st Floor,
222 Gray's Inn Road, London WC1X 8HB
www.simonandschuster.co.uk
Simon & Schuster Australia, Sydney
Simon & Schuster India, New Delhi

A CIP catalogue copy for this book is available from
the British Library.

Weight Watchers Publications Team:
Jane Griffiths, Cheryl Jackson, Nina McKerlie and
Imogen Prescott
Simon & Schuster Project Management:
WordWorks
Recipe testing: Sue Ashworth, Emma Marsden, Katie
Bishop
Photography: Lis Parsons
Prop styling: Jenny Iggleden
Food styling: Sue Ashworth
Design and typesetting: Jane Humphrey
Cover photography: Dan Jones
Cover food styling: Kim Morphew
Cover prop styling: Rachel Jukes
Cover design: Smith & Gilmour
Colour reproduction by Dot Gradations Ltd, UK
Printed and bound in Singapore

Pictured on the front cover: Pork, Turkey and Chorizo
Burgers, page 31
Pictured on the back cover, from top to bottom:
Sausage, Apple and Ginger Casserole, page 48;
Creamy Hazelnut Pasta, page 52; Spanish Chicken
Involtini, page 32; Camomile, Honey and Vanilla
Swiss Roll, page 70

Cuisinart

*Cuisinart have very kindly provided
the prizes for the competition.*

ProPoints® value logo:
You'll find this easy to read
ProPoints value logo on every recipe
throughout this book. The logo
represents the number of **ProPoints**
values per serving each recipe
contains. It is not an indication of the
fillingness of a recipe.

Weight Watchers **ProPoints** Weight
Loss System is a simple way to
lose weight. As part of the Weight
Watchers **ProPoints** plan you'll enjoy
eating delicious, healthy, filling foods
that help to keep you feeling satisfied
for longer and in control of your
portions.

Filling & Healthy Foods are
highlighted in green. Focus on these
foods where you can – they are
healthy choices that will help you to
feel satisfied for longer.

V This symbol denotes a vegetarian
recipe and assumes that, where
relevant, free range eggs, vegetarian
cheese, vegetarian virtually fat-free
fromage frais, vegetarian low fat
crème fraîche and vegetarian low fat
yogurts are used. Virtually fat-free
fromage frais, low fat crème fraîche
and low fat yogurts may contain
traces of gelatine so they are not
always vegetarian. Please check the
labels.

❋ This symbol denotes a dish that
can be frozen. Unless otherwise
stated, you can freeze the finished
dish for up to 3 months. Defrost
thoroughly and reheat until the dish
is piping hot throughout.

Recipe notes

Egg size: Medium unless otherwise
stated.
Raw eggs: Only the freshest eggs
should be used. Pregnant women,
the elderly and children should avoid
recipes with eggs which are not fully
cooked or raw.
All fruits and vegetables: Medium
unless otherwise stated.
Chocolate: Use chocolate with a
minimum of 70% cocoa solids.
Low fat spread: Where a recipe
states to use a low fat spread, a light
spread with a fat content of no less
than 38% should be used.
Stock: Stock cubes should be used
in the recipes, unless otherwise
stated. Prepare them according
to the packet instructions, unless
directed otherwise.
Microwaves: Microwave timings are
for an 850 watt microwave oven.
Recipe timings: These are
approximate and only meant to be
guidelines. Please note that the
preparation time includes all the
steps up to and following the main
cooking time(s). The cooking times
do not include lighting and heating
up the barbecue.
Low fat soft cheese: Where a
recipe states to use low fat soft
cheese, a soft cheese with a fat
content of less than 5% should
be used.
Recipe amends: Weight Watchers
has adjusted some recipe ingredients
and methods from the original
competition entries to either clarify
instructions or help Members to
maximise their **ProPoints** allowance.

contents

Enjoy the best of Weight Watchers very own Members' and Leaders' recipes in the latest cookbook from Weight Watchers. All the dishes in Members' Favourites were entered into the Weight Watcher Members and Leaders Recipe Competition, which received over 300 entries. A panel of judges deliberated over every entry before a shortlist was then tested by a team of professional home economists. The judging panel then selected the very best 72 recipes which are published here.

This book has been created by those who *live* the **ProPoints** plan and what better way to discover new recipes that not only taste great but have also helped our Members to stay on track. These are the recipes they rely on – the ones they turn to again and again, and now you can do the same. Plus we've calculated the **ProPoints** values for each recipe to make it even easier for you to follow the **ProPoints** plan.

A special thank you must go to our competition sponsors, Cuisinart. For over 30 years, Cuisinart's aim has been to produce the very finest kitchen equipment. All Cuisinart products are engineered for an exceptionally long life and are designed to be easy to use, as well as to give excellent performance day after day. For further information visit www.cuisinart.co.uk.

Every entrant with a recipe featured in the book received a Cuisinart elite mini food processor, and those lucky enough to win overall category winner took home a Cuisinart soup maker. Congratulations to all of our winners.

Cuisinart®

light meals, lunches
& snacks

Quorn with beetroot salad

Denni Frater, from Alkham, Kent, wanted to create a quick and tasty recipe and she has definitely succeeded. The contrast between the sweetness of the orange and the heat of the chilli and mustard is so unusual that our judges gave her a category winner award.

V Serves 2
6 *ProPoints* values per recipe
35 minutes in total

2 oranges
1–2 tablespoons Dijon mustard
140 g pack Quorn roast-style sliced fillets
1 tablespoon chilli and garlic sauce
1 red onion, sliced into thin half moons
250 g (9 oz) cooked beetroot (vacuum packed, not in vinegar), sliced
70 g bag rocket leaves
2 tablespoons low fat plain fromage frais
salt and freshly ground black pepper

1 Finely grate the zest from the oranges and mix with the Dijon mustard in a large bowl.

2 Over another large bowl, to catch all the juices, peel and cut the oranges into segments. Add 2 tablespoons of the orange juice to the orange zest and mustard mixture, along with the Quorn. Stir to coat, then put to one side.

3 Add the chilli and garlic sauce to the bowl with the orange segments and stir. Add the onion and beetroot, stirring gently to mix.

4 Heat a non stick frying pan and add the Quorn and its marinade. Cook over a low heat, turning the Quorn occasionally, for 5–6 minutes.

5 Tip the warm Quorn into the orange and beetroot salad and add the rocket leaves. Toss everything together and season to taste. Serve each portion topped with 1 tablespoon of fromage frais.

Try this
In step 4, you could use 140 g (5 oz) sliced skinless boneless chicken breast instead of Quorn, for the same ***ProPoints*** values per serving.

Cauliflower gratin d'Avril

A Weight Watchers member since the 1970s, *Avril Stocks* from Chertsey thinks the **ProPoints** plan is marvellous. She chose this recipe because it's delicious, inexpensive and so easy to make.

Serves 2
9 ProPoints values per recipe
25 minutes preparation, 20 minutes cooking

*4 rashers smoked or unsmoked lean
    back bacon, trimmed of visible fat
1 small cauliflower, broken into florets
1 small onion, diced
75 g (2¾ oz) reduced fat Cheddar cheese, grated
2 tomatoes, sliced
salt and freshly ground black pepper*

1 Preheat the grill to high and grill the bacon well. Cut into small pieces.

2 Preheat the oven to Gas Mark 5/190°C/fan oven 170°C.

3 Bring a saucepan of water to the boil, add the cauliflower and onion and cook until soft, but not mushy – about 10 minutes. Drain thoroughly, then mash well.

4 Add the bacon to the mashed cauliflower and onion mixture. Season to taste, then transfer to an ovenproof dish, measuring roughly 15 × 25 cm (6 x 10 inches).

5 Sprinkle the cheese evenly over the top, then arrange the sliced tomatoes over the cheese. Bake for 20 minutes then serve.

Cook's tip
Make sure the cauliflower and onion mixture is well drained before mashing, otherwise it will be soggy.

Spicy courgette and butternut squash soup

Carole McBride from Halton in Leeds has made several versions of this delicious soup and found that courgette and butternut squash make the best combination.

V ❋ Serves 4
2 ProPoints values per recipe
20 minutes preparation, 20 minutes cooking

*calorie controlled cooking spray
2 onions, chopped
500 g (1 lb 2 oz) butternut squash,
    peeled, de-seeded and chopped
2 large courgettes, chopped
2 teaspoons ground cumin
850 ml (1½ pints) vegetable stock
salt and freshly ground black pepper*

1 Spray a large saucepan with the cooking spray and place over a medium heat. Add the onion and soften for 3–4 minutes.

2 Add the butternut squash and courgettes, followed by the ground cumin, then cook for a further 2–3 minutes, stirring.

3 Pour in the stock, bring to the boil, then reduce the heat and simmer for 20 minutes until the vegetables are tender.

4 Remove from the heat. Using a food processor or hand-held blender, whizz until smooth. Season to taste, then serve in warmed bowls.

Try this
Use 1 teaspoon dried chilli flakes instead of the ground cumin for the same **ProPoints** values per serving.

Twice-baked smoked salmon soufflés

Barbara Larner from Tamworth has been a Gold Member since 1995. This winning recipe always impresses her dinner guests and is very low in **ProPoints** values. It can be made ahead of time and then reheated when needed.

Serves 8
19 ProPoints values per recipe
20 minutes preparation + chilling, 30 minutes cooking

15 g (½ oz) butter, melted
25 g (1 oz) dried breadcrumbs
20 g (¾ oz) cornflour
300 ml (10 fl oz) skimmed milk
a pinch of cayenne pepper
juice of ½ a lime
2 egg yolks
100 g (3½ oz) smoked salmon, chopped finely
5 egg whites
salt and freshly ground black pepper

1 Preheat the oven to Gas Mark 5/190°C/fan oven 170°C.

2 Brush the insides of eight 9 cm (3½ inch) ramekins with the melted butter. Coat each with the dried breadcrumbs.

3 Put the cornflour in a medium saucepan. Over a low heat, gradually add the milk, blending until smooth. Bring to the boil, then simmer for 1–2 minutes, stirring constantly to make a fairly thick white sauce. Remove from the heat and season with the cayenne pepper, seasoning and lime juice. Set aside to cool.

4 Beat the two egg yolks into the cooled white sauce and then mix in the salmon.

5 In a large grease-free bowl, whisk the egg whites until they form soft peaks. Using a large metal spoon, carefully fold the egg whites into the salmon mixture.

6 Spoon the mixture into the ramekins. Place in a roasting tin with enough hot water to come halfway up the sides of the ramekins.

7 Bake for 18–20 minutes, until well risen and brown. Remove from the oven, cool, then chill.

8 When ready to serve, preheat the oven to Gas Mark 5/190°C/fan oven 170°C. Put the chilled ramekins in a tin and add hot water then leave for a few minutes, as this will make them easier to turn out.

9 Remove the ramekins from the tin and run a knife around the insides of them. Turn them out on to a baking tray. Bake for 12 minutes. They will puff up again and the outsides will become crisp. Serve immediately.

Spicy Chinese soup

Karin Snellock from Martinstown in Dorset joined Weight Watchers with her husband Nick, and they have both reached their goal weight. For them, the most important thing in a recipe is lots of flavour so Karin has created a very delicious and low *ProPoints* value vegetable soup.

V ❄ Serves 4
1 *ProPoints* value per recipe
30 minutes in total

4 tablespoons reduced salt soy sauce
2 carrots, peeled and sliced into large matchsticks
200 g can bamboo shoots, drained and sliced
    into large matchsticks
75 g (2¾ oz) shiitake mushrooms, sliced
2½ cm (1 inch) fresh root ginger, peeled
    and grated
1 tablespoon chopped spring onions
2 pak choi, stalks and leaves chopped separately
salt and freshly ground black pepper

1 Bring 850 ml (1½ pints) water to the boil in a large saucepan and add the soy sauce, carrots, bamboo shoots, mushrooms, ginger and spring onions. Bring back to the boil, then reduce the heat and simmer for 10 minutes.
2 Add the pak choi stalks to the saucepan and simmer for 5 minutes, then add the pak choi leaves. Check the seasoning, adding more soy sauce if needed. Serve when the pak choi leaves have just wilted.

Try this
For a spicier version, add a de-seeded and chopped red or green fresh chilli with the ginger.

Warm salad Niçoise with cod

This delicious variation of the traditional French salad was created by *Michelle Wyckoff-Smith* from Muswell Hill, London. It's quick to prepare and makes a fantastic Friday night meal.

Serves 2
16 *ProPoints* values per recipe
15 minutes preparation, 45 minutes cooking

200 g (7 oz) new potatoes
175 g (6 oz) green beans, trimmed
10 olives in brine, drained
15 g (½ oz) capers in brine, drained
100 ml (3½ fl oz) white wine
1 tablespoon olive oil
150 g (5½ oz) cherry tomatoes
2 × 125 g (4½ oz) cod fillets
salt and freshly ground black pepper
a handful of fresh basil leaves, torn, to garnish

1 Preheat the oven to Gas Mark 6/200°C/fan oven 180°C.
2 Bring a saucepan of water to the boil, add the potatoes and cook for about 15 minutes, until tender. Add the green beans and blanch for 2 minutes.
3 Drain thoroughly, then put the potatoes and beans in a shallow baking dish. Add the olives, capers, wine and olive oil, tossing them all together. Cook in the oven for 20 minutes.
4 Remove from the oven, add the tomatoes and toss together, then place the cod fillets on top of the vegetables. Season the cod, return to the oven and roast for a further 10 minutes.
5 Divide the vegetables and cod between two serving plates. Garnish with the basil leaves and serve immediately.

Try this
Other fish can be substituted for the cod. Try 2 x 130 g (4½ oz) salmon steaks for 12 *ProPoints* values per serving, or 2 × 140 g (5 oz) tuna steaks for 10 *ProPoints* values per serving.

A few creative twists turn this classic salad into something really satisfying. The fillets make it filling and the flavours are fantastic.

Courgette and cheese soup

A Gold member for 15 years, *Alice Wheeler* from Fife in Scotland loves this creamy soup because it's so easy to make.

V ✳ Serves 6

16 *ProPoints* values per recipe

10 minutes preparation + cooling, 20 minutes cooking

2 vegetable stock cubes
1 onion, chopped
450 g (1 lb) courgettes, sliced
300 g (10½ oz) potatoes, peeled and chopped
200 g (7 oz) low fat soft cheese
salt and freshly ground black pepper
a handful of chopped fresh parsley, to garnish

1 In a lidded saucepan, bring 850 ml (1½ pints) water to the boil and add all the ingredients, apart from the cheese.

2 Cover with a lid, bring back to the boil, then reduce the heat and simmer gently for 15–20 minutes, until the vegetables are tender. Allow to cool slightly.

3 Add the soft cheese then transfer to a food processor or hand-held blender and whizz until smooth. Season to taste, then serve sprinkled with the parsley.

Cook's tip
If you grow courgettes, this is a brilliant way to use them.

Cambodian chicken salad

Kate Blanks from Great Baddow in Essex loves cooking and has created a recipe that's light, easy and full of flavour, yet low in *ProPoints* values. This recipe also works well with 2 x 130 g (5 oz) salmon steaks for 8 *ProPoints* values per serving, or 300 g (10½ oz) tofu for 7 *ProPoints* values per serving.

Serves 4

29 *ProPoints* values per recipe

25 minutes in total

125 g (4½ oz) dried rice noodles
½ cucumber
2 x 120 g (4½ oz) cooked skinless boneless chicken breasts, shredded
2 carrots, peeled and cut into matchsticks
60 g (2 oz) beansprouts
½ mango, peeled and diced
1 tablespoon roughly chopped fresh mint, parsley or chives, plus extra to garnish
25 g (1 oz) salted peanuts

For the dressing
zest and juice of ½ a lime
2 tablespoons soft brown sugar
2 tablespoons rice vinegar
2 tablespoons fish sauce
1 long green or red fresh chilli, de-seeded if required, chopped finely
salt and freshly ground black pepper

1 Bring a saucepan of water to the boil, add the noodles and cook according to the packet instructions. Drain, then run under cold water and drain again thoroughly.

2 Halve the cucumber lengthways, scoop out the seeds with a teaspoon, then pare into ribbons using a vegetable peeler. Put the noodles and cucumber in a large bowl. Add the chicken, carrots, beansprouts, mango and mint, parsley or chives. Mix together.

3 For the dressing, mix all the ingredients together in a screw-top jar, or similar. Shake then pour over the salad.

4 To serve, arrange on plates and scatter the peanuts on top, along with the extra herbs.

Spicy roasted tomato soup

Faye Clark from St Leonards, East Kilbride, came up with this fantastic zero **ProPoints** value soup one evening using only what she had in her fridge. It's a hit with both her husband and her friends.

V ❄ Serves 4
1 ProPoints value per recipe
15 minutes preparation, 25 minutes cooking

8 tomatoes, *chopped roughly*
2 garlic cloves, *chopped roughly*
1 fresh chilli, *de-seeded and chopped roughly*
2 red onions, *chopped roughly*
1 red or yellow pepper, *de-seeded and chopped roughly*
calorie-controlled cooking spray
1 teaspoon mixed dried herbs
1 litre (1¾ pints) vegetable stock
salt and freshly ground black pepper

1 Preheat the oven to Gas Mark 4/180°C/fan oven 160°C.

2 Put the tomatoes, garlic, chilli, onions and pepper in a roasting tin. Spray with cooking spray, add the mixed herbs and toss together.

3 Roast in the oven for 10 minutes, then turn the vegetables over and roast for a further 10–15 minutes, until slightly charred.

4 Put the roasted vegetables into a large saucepan and add the stock. Bring to the boil then, using a food processor or hand-held blender, whizz until smooth. Season to taste, then serve.

Try this

For a creamier texture and flavour, add 100 g (3½ oz) low fat soft cheese and blend it with the vegetables, for 1 **ProPoints** value per serving.

In the summer, chill the soup until icy cold to serve as a version of gazpacho. If you like, set aside a few of the vegetables for garnishing the soup before blending, then sprinkle them on top with a few fresh basil leaves.

Sausage savouries

If you're looking for a recipe that fits in with everyday life, then look no further. *Karen Petitt* of Thetford, Norfolk, finds that these savouries are ideal for lunch boxes, picnics and even for bringing to work for her colleagues.

❄ Makes 24
56 *ProPoints* values per recipe
30 minutes in total

calorie controlled cooking spray
2 tablespoons plain flour, for dusting
375 g (13 oz) ready-rolled shortcrust pastry sheet
4 Weight Watchers sausages (Premium or Cumberland)
1 small onion, chopped finely
3 tablespoons skimmed milk

1 Preheat the oven to Gas Mark 6/200°C/fan oven 180°C. Spray two baking sheets with cooking spray.

2 Sprinkle a work surface with a little flour and lay the pastry sheet on top. Use a floured rolling pin to roll out the sheet a little larger and then use a plain 8 cm (3¼ inch) cutter to stamp out as many circles as possible. Re-roll the trimmings and cut out more circles until the pastry is used up and you have 24 circles.

3 Remove the skins from the sausages and share the meat from each one between six circles. Top with some of the chopped onion, then dampen the outer edge of the pastry with a little milk. Fold over and seal, pinching the edges together. Make three small cuts into the top of each one with a sharp knife.

4 Arrange the pasties on the prepared trays and brush with the remaining milk. Bake in the oven for 10–12 minutes until golden brown. Serve hot or cold.

Try this
Make the pasties with 2 × 80 g cans tuna instead of the sausages, using the onion as above for the same ***ProPoints*** values per serving.

Low fat Scotch eggs

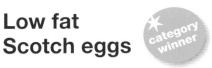

This winning recipe from *Susan Sherratt* of Porthmadog, Gwynedd, is perfect for a light lunch, buffet or picnic. It's one of her husband's favourites and he likes to take a Scotch egg to work in his packed lunch.

❄ Serves 2
11 *ProPoints* values per recipe
15 minutes preparation, 30 minutes cooking

2 eggs
½ medium slice white bread
2 × 40 g (1½ oz) low fat sausages
1 teaspoon flour (any type)
1 egg white, whisked lightly
calorie controlled cooking spray

1 Bring a small pan of water to the boil, add the eggs and cook for 12 minutes. Meanwhile, using a food processor or hand-held blender, whizz the bread to make breadcrumbs. Drain the eggs and plunge them into a bowl of cold water. (This prevents them from cooking any longer, and stops a black ring from forming around the yolk.) When cool enough to handle, peel.

2 Preheat the oven to Gas Mark 6/200°C/fan oven 180°C.

3 Remove the skins from the sausages and, one at a time, with damp palms, press the meat from each sausage into a rough oval shape. Put the egg on the sausage meat, and again with damp hands, mould the sausage meat around the egg until completely encased. Repeat with the second egg.

4 Dust both eggs with flour – this helps the egg white to stick. Roll the eggs in the egg white, then roll in the breadcrumbs. Place them on a wire rack positioned over a roasting tin or baking sheet. Spray both eggs with cooking spray.

5 Bake for 30 minutes, making sure that the sausage meat is cooked. Serve hot or cold.

Serving suggestion
Serve with a crisp green salad for no extra ***ProPoints*** values.

*If you long for a Scotch egg,
why not try this home-made
version? The flavours and
textures are so fresh-tasting,
it's sure to become a favourite.*

Stilton pâté and pears

Anne de Normanville from Reigate, Surrey, loves blue cheese but not its high **ProPoints** values. She came up with this recipe so she could enjoy the taste without using up much of her **ProPoints** value budget. It's fantastic any time of year.

V ❄ Serves 4
18 ProPoints values per recipe
15 minutes in total

50 g (1¾ oz) Stilton cheese, crumbled
50 g (1¾ oz) Quark
1 tablespoon 0% fat Greek yogurt
1 tablespoon chopped walnuts
a pinch of nutmeg
2 ripe pears
juice of ½ a lemon
freshly ground black pepper
To serve
watercress
24 Melba toasts

1 To make the pâté, put the cheese in a small bowl. Add the Quark and yogurt and use a fork to mash together. Stir in the walnuts. Season with a little pepper and grated nutmeg, to taste. Cover and chill in the fridge until ready to serve.

2 Just before serving, peel, halve and core the pears. Cut each half into four slices and sprinkle with lemon juice to prevent discolouration.

3 Arrange four pear slices on each plate with some watercress. Share the pâté between the plates and serve with six Melba toasts each.

Cook's tip

This makes a refreshing light lunch, or it could be served as a starter.

Try this

At Christmas, the pâté can be jazzed up a little with 1 tablespoon Port, adding 1 extra **ProPoints** value per serving.

Potato cakes with feta

Hazel Linley from Sheffield, South Yorkshire, always gets lots of compliments when she cooks this dish. The cakes are ideal for packed lunches, buffets or picnics and it's a great recipe for using up leftover potatoes.

V ❄ Serves 4
19 ProPoints values per recipe
20 minutes preparation + 1 hour chilling,
45 minutes cooking

500 g (1 lb 2 oz) floury potatoes
    (e.g. King Edward), unpeeled
4 spring onions
2 teaspoons chopped fresh thyme
1 egg, beaten
1 tablespoon lemon juice
115 g (4¼ oz) light feta cheese
1 tablespoon plain flour, for dusting
calorie controlled cooking spray
salt and freshly ground black pepper
To serve
a few salad leaves
a handful of chopped fresh chives

1 Bring a lidded saucepan of water to the boil, add the potatoes and cook for 25 minutes. Drain, cool slightly, then peel.

2 Mash the potatoes in a large bowl, then add the remaining ingredients, apart from the flour. Mix well, but take care not to break up the feta too much. Season, then cover and refrigerate for a minimum of 1 hour, though best if left overnight.

3 Divide the mixture into 12 balls. Roll and flatten with the palm of your hand, then dust with a little flour.

4 Preheat the oven to Gas Mark 7/220°C/fan oven 200°C. Spray the potato cakes with cooking spray and either fry in a non stick frying pan for 3–4 minutes per side, or bake for 15–20 minutes, until golden brown.

5 Allow three potato cakes per person. Serve with the salad leaves, garnished with chopped chives.

Cook's tip

Try serving this with 70 g (2½ oz) baked beans and a poached egg per person for a total of 8 **ProPoints** values per serving.

Spinach, leek and mozzarella parcels

Marleen Haas from Great Cambourne, Cambridgeshire, loves experimenting with food. She created these samosa-like parcels with a few leftover vegetables in her fridge.

V ✳ Makes 12

13 ProPoints values per recipe

20 minutes preparation, 15 minutes cooking

calorie controlled cooking spray
1 onion, chopped
2 leeks, sliced
150 g (5½ oz) spinach
3 tablespoons vegetable stock or water
125 g (4½ oz) mozzarella light, drained
    and chopped into cubes
2 x 45 g (1½ oz) sheets filo pastry, each sheet measuring
    50 x 24 cm (20 x 9½ inches), defrosted if frozen
salt and freshly ground black pepper

1 Preheat the oven to Gas Mark 6/200°C/fan oven 180°C. Prepare a baking sheet, covering it with a piece of baking parchment.

2 Heat a large non stick frying pan or wok and spray with the cooking spray. Add the onion and cook for a few minutes, until soft. Add the leeks and sauté for a few minutes, then add the spinach.

3 Add the vegetable stock or water and season to taste. Once the spinach has wilted, remove from the heat and leave to cool.

4 Add the mozzarella to the cooled spinach mixture (but don't add it too soon as you don't want it to melt yet).

5 Cut each sheet of pastry in half to make four sheets and then cut each sheet into three strips lengthways. Divide the spinach mixture equally among the bottom left hand corners of the pastry strips. Fold the pastry strips over into triangles, like samosas.

6 Spray the parcels with cooking spray and arrange on the baking sheet. Bake in the oven for 15 minutes, or until golden brown and crispy.

main meals

category winner

Caribbean chicken

 8 ProPoints value

A teacher from Brecks, Rotherham, *Julia Johnson*, created this for Red Nose Day 2011, which explains all the red ingredients. Julia's recipe impressed the Weight Watchers judges so much she was awarded our grand prize for the Main Meals category.

Serves 4
33 *ProPoints* values per recipe
40 minutes in total

600 g (1 lb 5 oz) sweet potatoes, *cut into wedges*
2 teaspoons olive oil
1 teaspoon chilli flakes
calorie controlled cooking spray
2 garlic cloves, *crushed*
1 red fresh chilli, *de-seeded and sliced thinly*
500 g (1 lb 2 oz) skinless boneless chicken breasts, *cut into strips*
2 red peppers, *de-seeded and sliced*
2 red onions, *sliced*
2 large tomatoes, *chopped*
420 g can chopped tomatoes
1 banana, *sliced*
8 pineapple *rings in natural juice, drained and cut into chunks*
2 tablespoons sweet chilli sauce
salt and freshly ground black pepper

1 Preheat the oven to Gas Mark 6/200°C/fan oven 180°C. Toss the sweet potatoes in the olive oil with the chilli flakes and a little salt. Spread out on a non stick baking sheet. Bake for 30–35 minutes until golden and tender.

2 Meanwhile, spray a wok or large non stick frying pan with cooking spray. Add the garlic and chilli then add the chicken and brown slightly. Add the peppers and onions and cook, stirring often, for 10 minutes.

3 Add the fresh tomatoes and cook for 2 minutes, then add the canned tomatoes and simmer for 10 minutes. Add the banana, pineapple and chilli sauce for the final 2 minutes to heat through. Serve with the sweet potato wedges.

Beef risotto

This tasty winter warmer from *Colin Banks* of Walthamstow is easy to prepare and great to share with family and friends.

Serves 6
56 *ProPoints* values per recipe
35 minutes preparation, 55 minutes cooking

350 g (12 oz) dried risotto rice
½ a kettleful of boiling water
1 tablespoon olive oil
350 g (12 oz) lean braising steak, cut into 5 mm (¼ inch)
    strips
1 onion, halved and sliced
½ green pepper, de-seeded and cut into strips
½ red pepper, de-seeded and cut into strips
2 beef tomatoes, halved and sliced
3 bay leaves
2 teaspoons dried Provençal herbs
2 teaspoons Worcestershire sauce
175 ml (6 fl oz) red wine
1.2 litres beef stock (made with 2 stock cubes)
400 g can French or whole green beans, drained
salt and freshly ground black pepper

1 In a sieve, rinse the rice thoroughly under cold running water. Put the rice in a medium saucepan, cover with about 1 litre (1¾ pints) cold water and bring to the boil, then simmer for 5 minutes. Drain thoroughly then rinse with boiling water. Drain again and set aside.

2 Warm the oil in a large, lidded, flameproof casserole dish over a high heat. Add the beef strips and cook in batches for 5–10 minutes until dark brown all over. Add the onion and peppers and continue cooking for a further 5 minutes until starting to soften.

3 Add the tomatoes, bay leaves, herbs, Worcestershire sauce, wine and stock. Bring to the boil then reduce the heat and simmer for 45 minutes until the meat is tender.

4 Stir in the rice and green beans. Bring to the boil then simmer gently, uncovered, for a further 10 minutes, until the rice is tender and the cooking liquid has almost been absorbed. Remove from the heat and leave to rest for 5 minutes then season to taste and serve.

Thai tuna

Her love of interesting food led *Kate Sparrow* from Martock, Somerset, to send in this recipe in which she makes the most of the wonderful flavours of Thailand.

Serves 4
53 *ProPoints* values per recipe
35 minutes in total + marinating

For the marinade
3 tablespoons lemon juice
3 tablespoons lime juice
100 ml (3½ oz) light soy sauce
1 teaspoon sesame oil
1 garlic clove, crushed
5 g (¼ oz) pine nut kernels, chopped roughly
1 tablespoon desiccated coconut
5 kaffir lime leaves
For the tuna and noodles
4 × 150 g (5½ oz) tuna steaks
250 g (9 oz) dried medium egg noodles
5 g (¼ oz) pine nut kernels, chopped roughly
To garnish
shredded lettuce
chopped spring onions
½ cucumber, sliced
8 lime wedges

1 First, make the marinade. Combine all the ingredients in a bowl and mix well. Put the tuna in a shallow dish large enough to take the steaks in a single layer. Pour over the marinade and turn the fish so that it is well coated. Cover and place in the fridge for at least 30 minutes or for up to 2 hours, turning occasionally.

2 Remove the tuna from the marinade then pour the marinade into a small pan. Bring to the boil over a high heat. Cook for 5 minutes until slightly reduced then remove the lime leaves.

3 Meanwhile, bring a medium saucepan of water to the boil, add the noodles and cook for 3–4 minutes, or according to packet instructions. Drain.

4 Warm a non stick frying pan or griddle over a high heat. Cook the tuna for 2–4 minutes on each side depending on how rare you like it. Divide the noodles between four plates or shallow bowls, sprinkle over the remaining pine nut kernels and top with the tuna. Serve with the marinade drizzled over, and the garnishes on the side.

Romanesque chicken

Deborah Glennie from Wellington in Somerset is a member of an Iron Age/Roman historic re-creation society. She chose this recipe, based on an ancient Roman dish, for its distinctive Roman flavours. Full of spices, it's ideal served with zero **ProPoints** value vegetables.

❄ Serves 4
36 ProPoints values per recipe
20 minutes preparation, 50 minutes cooking

calorie controlled cooking spray
4 × 150 g (5½ oz) skinless boneless chicken breasts
½ teaspoon ground black pepper
1 teaspoon fresh thyme
½ teaspoon cumin seeds
½ teaspoon fennel seeds
1 teaspoon chopped fresh mint
½ teaspoon chopped fresh rosemary
1 teaspoon honey
500 ml (18 fl oz) chicken stock
2 teaspoons olive oil
1 teaspoon white wine vinegar
100 g (3½ oz) medjool dates, pitted and chopped
400 g (14 oz) new potatoes

1 Preheat the grill to medium-high. Spray the chicken breasts with cooking spray and grill for 20 minutes, turning once.

2 Meanwhile, grind together the pepper, thyme, cumin seeds, fennel seeds, mint and rosemary using a pestle and mortar or a small food processor, or just chop extra finely.

3 Put the honey, stock and olive oil in a large saucepan. Blend the ground spices with the vinegar and add them to the saucepan with the dates. Bring to the boil and add the grilled chicken. Cover and simmer over a low heat for 30 minutes.

4 Meanwhile, bring a saucepan of water to the boil, add the potatoes and cook until tender. Serve with the chicken.

Vegetable chick pea balti

A Gold Member from Whoberley, Coventry, *Valerie Elvin* joined Weight Watchers 23 years ago. She chose this recipe because it's a great alternative to a takeaway and delicious to serve to guests.

V ❄ Serves 4
30 ProPoints values per recipe
15 minutes preparation, 35 minutes cooking

1 teaspoon vegetable oil
2 carrots, peeled and chopped
2 small onions, chopped
225 g (8 oz) potato, chopped
150 g (5½ oz) mushrooms, sliced
1 courgette, chopped
1½ red, yellow or green peppers, de-seeded and chopped
1 small leek, white stalk chopped, green part discarded
3 tablespoons balti curry paste
1 vegetable stock cube
75 g (2¾ oz) tomato purée
75 g (2¾ oz) dried red lentils
200 g (7 oz) canned chick peas, rinsed and drained
600 ml (20 fl oz) boiling water
salt and freshly ground black pepper
15 g (½ oz) chopped fresh coriander, plus sprigs, to garnish

1 Heat the oil in a large, lidded, saucepan and add all the chopped vegetables. Lightly fry until beginning to soften, about 15 minutes. Season.

2 Stir in the curry paste and crumble in the stock cube, then add the tomato purée, lentils and chick peas. Give everything a good stir, then pour in the boiling water.

3 Cover and simmer over a low heat for 15–20 minutes until the potato is soft and the lentils are cooked. Stir in the coriander and serve, garnished with extra sprigs.

Vietnamese fish

Elaine Mooney has been a Leader in Woolton near Liverpool for 2½ years and loves to get the Members excited about cooking. She created this recipe in Vietnam where she cooked it on a primus stove in the garden of a restaurant in Hoi An. The aromas and flavours are simply wonderful. And the fish counter in your supermarket can prepare the fish for you.

Serves 2
14 *ProPoints* values per recipe
25 minutes preparation, 20 minutes cooking

400 g (14 oz) whole sea bass, *gutted and scaled*
1 tablespoon vegetable oil
3 shallots, *sliced*
3 spring onions, *sliced finely*
1 lemongrass *stalk, sliced finely*
5 cm (2 inch) piece fresh root ginger,
    peeled and sliced finely
3 garlic cloves, *crushed*
a pinch of sugar
freshly ground black pepper
For the sauce
juice of 1 lemon
½ teaspoon salt
½ teaspoon sugar
½ teaspoon freshly ground black pepper

1 Preheat the oven to Gas Mark 6/200°C/fan oven 180°C, or if barbecuing, heat the barbecue.

2 Make a deep pocket at an angle on both sides of the fish with a sharp knife.

3 Heat the oil in a non stick frying pan and fry the shallots until crisp. Remove from the pan and drain on kitchen paper. Add the spring onions to the pan and fry gently until softened.

4 Mix together the shallots, spring onions, lemongrass, ginger, garlic, sugar and pepper. Stuff this mixture into the pockets on both sides of the fish. Spray a large sheet of foil with cooking spray. Put the fish on top and wrap well.

5 Place in the oven and bake for 15–20 minutes, turning the fish over after 10 minutes. If cooking on the barbecue, cook for 10 minutes on each side.

6 Mix together the sauce ingredients. Remove the skin and bones from the fish. Pour over the sauce, then serve.

Sweet honey and orange veggie bake

This filling recipe by *Emma Pooley*, from Rugby in Warwickshire, has a delicious sweetness. It's popular with friends and family who aren't following the Weight Watchers plan too and goes well with most vegetables so why not experiment?

V Serves 2
8 *ProPoints* values per recipe
40 minutes in total

calorie controlled cooking spray
500 g (1 lb 2 oz) cooking apples, *peeled, cored
    and cut into 1–2 inch cubes*
300 g (10½ oz) butternut squash, *peeled,
    de-seeded and cut into 1 cm (½ inch) cubes*
1 red onion, *diced*
1 onion, *diced*
4 spring onions, *trimmed and sliced thinly lengthways*
1 green pepper, *de-seeded and diced*
finely grated zest and juice of 1 orange
1 teaspoon ground ginger
2½ tablespoons light soy sauce
2½ tablespoons clear honey
4 teaspoons cornflour

1 Preheat the oven to Gas Mark 6/200°C/fan oven 180°C.

2 Heat a large, deep, non stick frying pan or wok over a high heat and spray with the cooking spray. Add the apples and prepared vegetables and cook for 5–10 minutes, stirring often, until just starting to soften. Remove from the heat.

3 Meanwhile, put the orange zest in a small saucepan. Add the orange juice, ginger, soy sauce, honey and cornflour and mix well. Warm over a high heat for 1–2 minutes, stirring continuously until just starting to bubble.

4 Mix the sauce into the vegetables. Spoon the mixture into a 23 × 30 cm (9 × 12 inch) ovenproof dish and bake for 10 minutes until piping hot and starting to colour. Serve immediately.

Thai style chicken noodle broth

Mother of two, *Alison Munro* of Gourock, Scotland, recommends this very tasty dish, and it's a great way to use up leftover roast chicken. If you want to use fresh stock instead of cubes, remember to add the extra *ProPoints* values.

Serves 2
11 *ProPoints* values per recipe
35 minutes in total

500 ml (18 fl oz) chicken stock
1 shallot or ½ small red onion, sliced thinly
2½ cm (1 inch) fresh root ginger, grated finely
1 garlic clove, grated finely
1–2 bird's eye chillies, sliced thinly, plus
    extra to serve
1–2 lemongrass stalks, trimmed and sliced thinly
juice and finely grated zest of a lime, plus 2 wedges
    to serve
2 heads pak choi
75 g (2¾ oz) mushrooms, sliced
120 g (4½ oz) cooked skinless chicken breast, shredded
2 teaspoons fish sauce
2–4 tablespoons roughly chopped fresh coriander, plus
    extra to serve
60 g (2 oz) dried fine egg noodles

1 Pour the chicken stock into a large saucepan and bring to the boil.

2 Reduce the heat to low and add the shallot or onion, ginger, garlic, chillies, lemongrass, and the finely grated zest from the lime. Simmer gently for 10 minutes until slightly reduced.

3 Shred the white part of the pak choi stalks thinly. Add them to the pan along with the mushrooms, chicken and fish sauce. Simmer for a further 5 minutes until piping hot. Remove from the heat and add the lime juice, coriander and tops from the pak choi.

4 Meanwhile, bring a small saucepan of water to the boil, add the noodles and cook according to the packet instructions until tender, then drain.

5 Divide the noodles between two bowls then ladle over the hot broth. Garnish with the extra coriander and chilli. Serve some lime wedges alongside for squeezing.

Cauliflower risotto

Housewife and mother of two *Lindsey MacWilliam* of Burpham, Surrey, loves to cook and share her creations.

V Serves 4

37 ProPoints values per recipe

40 minutes in total

850 ml (1½ pints) vegetable stock
850 g (1 lb 12½ oz) cauliflower, *cut into florets*
2 tablespoons olive oil
200 g (7 oz) leek, *trimmed and chopped finely*
2 spring onions, *trimmed and chopped finely*
2 garlic cloves, *1 chopped finely and 1 crushed*
½ teaspoon ground cumin
½ teaspoon ground coriander
200 g (7 oz) dried white Arborio rice
125 ml (4 fl oz) dry white wine
40 g (1½ oz) medium slice white bread
½–1 teaspoon crushed dried chilli, to taste
2 tablespoons grated Parmesan cheese

1 Put the stock in a large 1.2 litre (2 pint) saucepan and bring to the boil. Add the cauliflower, return to the boil and cook for 3 minutes until just tender. Remove and set aside, and keep the stock warm over a low heat.

2 Meanwhile, warm half of the oil in a heavy-bottomed pan over a medium heat. Add the leek, half of the spring onions and half of the garlic. Mix in the cumin and coriander. Fry gently for 5 minutes until soft.

3 Add the rice and stir gently until the grains are well coated in the oil. Stir in the wine until all the liquid has been absorbed. Add a ladle of the hot stock and stir frequently until the liquid has been absorbed. Repeat this process for about 20 minutes, or until all the stock has been used and the rice is creamy and tender.

4 Meanwhile, using a food processor or hand-held blender, whizz the bread to make fine crumbs. Warm the remaining oil in a small frying pan over a high heat. Add the breadcrumbs, remaining spring onions, garlic and crushed chilli. Fry for 2–3 minutes until golden. Remove from the heat and cool in the pan.

5 Gently fold the cauliflower and half of the cheese into the risotto. Remove from the heat and leave to rest for 3–5 minutes. Stir the remaining cheese into the breadcrumb mixture and serve sprinkled over the risotto.

Italian lamb

Michael Clarkson from Sketty, Swansea, likes this dish because it looks fantastic, tastes elegant and is easy to prepare and cook. For the best flavour, he recommends cooking the lamb over mesquite charcoal.

✳ Serves 6

59 ProPoints values per recipe

15 minutes preparation + chilling + resting,

30 minutes cooking

1 kg (2 lb 4 oz) boneless leg of lamb
50 g (1¾ oz) prosciutto
50 g tin anchovies in olive oil, drained but
    reserving 1 tablespoon oil
3 garlic cloves
20 g (¾ oz) fresh flat leaf parsley
10 g (⅓ oz) fresh mint, *leaves only*
1 teaspoon finely chopped fresh rosemary leaves
1 tablespoon balsamic vinegar
freshly ground black pepper

1 Open out the lamb so it is flat against the work surface. Cut several diagonal slits across the meat about 8 mm (⅜ inch) deep and 5 cm (2 inches) apart.

2 Put all the remaining ingredients, including the reserved oil from the anchovies, in a food processor and whizz to make a smooth paste (alternatively chop everything as finely as possible). Season with black pepper.

3 Rub the paste over the cut side of the meat, being careful to push the mixture deep into the slits. Push two long metal skewers diagonally into the lamb so they cross over and make an 'X' shape. Place the meat on a non-metallic tray or dish, cover and chill for at least 2 hours and up to 12 hours.

4 Preheat the barbecue or grill to a medium-high heat. Cook the meat for 15 minutes on each side until well browned. Remove from the grill, place on a board and cover with foil. Leave to rest for 15 minutes before carving.

Cook's tip

If you prefer your lamb well done, cook it for an extra 5 minutes on each side.

Anchovies are often used in traditional Italian dishes to add a rich flavour. They certainly add something special to the marinade for this tasty and tender leg of lamb.

Tarragon chicken thighs

This easy-to-prepare recipe comes from *Karry Cowell*, of Poulton-le-Fylde, Lancashire, and is a great way to prepare chicken thighs. She chose this recipe because every time she makes it for her husband and family they are full of compliments. Serve with rice or pasta, remembering to add the extra **ProPoints** values.

❋ Serves 4
34 ProPoints values per recipe
10 minutes preparation, 2 hours cooking

600 g (1 lb 5 oz) skinless boneless chicken thighs
1 tablespoon roughly chopped fresh tarragon
    or 2 teaspoons dried tarragon
850 ml (1½ pints) chicken stock
2 large leeks, chopped roughly
3 tablespoons reduced fat crème fraîche
freshly ground black pepper

1 Preheat the oven to Gas Mark 4/180°C/fan oven 160°C.

2 Place the chicken thighs in a large ovenproof dish with a tight-fitting lid, add the tarragon to the stock and pour over the chicken. Season with black pepper.

3 Scatter the leeks over the top of the chicken. Cover and cook for 2 hours.

4 When cooked, stir in the crème fraîche and serve.

Try this
You could use 4 × 150 g (5½ oz) skinless boneless chicken breasts, if you prefer, for 5 **ProPoints** values per serving.

Sri Lankan pineapple curry

Wife and mum *Vicki Patterson* from Baldock in Hertfordshire was inspired to cook this recipe while on holiday in Sri Lanka. All her friends and family love it. Preparing fresh pineapple is very easy too so do try it.

V Serves 2
20 ProPoints values per recipe
45 minutes in total

125 g (4½ oz) dried basmati rice
calorie controlled cooking spray
2 small red onions, sliced thinly
5 large garlic cloves, crushed
1 cinnamon stick, broken into pieces
20 dried curry leaves
1 heaped teaspoon mild curry powder
¼ teaspoon turmeric
1 heaped teaspoon crushed chilli flakes
1 pineapple, peeled, 'eyes' and woody core removed,
    and sliced thinly lengthways (see Cook's tip)
200 ml (7 fl oz) reduced fat coconut milk
1 teaspoon sugar

1 Bring a saucepan of water to the boil, add the rice and cook according to packet instructions. Drain thoroughly.

2 Meanwhile, spray a lidded flameproof casserole dish with the cooking spray and place over a low heat. Fry the onions and garlic for about 10 minutes until softened, adding a splash of water if they start to stick. Add the cinnamon, curry leaves, curry powder, turmeric and chilli flakes and cook for 1 minute.

3 Stir in the pineapple and toss to coat in the spices. Pour over the coconut milk, then cover and cook over a low heat for 10 minutes. Stir in the sugar.

4 Divide the rice among two plates and serve the pineapple curry on top.

Cook's tip
To prepare a whole fresh pineapple, cut off the leaves and the base using a sharp knife then stand the pineapple upright and remove the peel by cutting downwards in a sawing motion. Remove any 'eyes' with the tip of your knife. Cut lengthways into quarters, remove the woody core and then slice.

Lamb moussaka

After reaching her goal weight, *Penny Phillips* from Catford was inspired to become a Leader. She loves moussaka but was often put off by the high **ProPoints** values, so she experimented with different options and came up with the delicious version below.

✳ Serves 6
52 ProPoints values per recipe
45 minutes preparation + cooling + resting,
1 hour 40 minutes cooking

500 g (1 lb 2 oz) lean lamb mince
1 tablespoon olive oil
1 onion, diced
175 ml (6 fl oz) dry white wine
2 × 400 g cans chopped tomatoes
100 g (3½ oz) mushrooms, sliced
3 garlic cloves, peeled and sliced
1 tablespoon dried oregano
2 bay leaves
1 teaspoon fresh thyme leaves
¼ teaspoon ground cinnamon
¼ teaspoon ground allspice
500 g (1 lb 2 oz) aubergines
For the topping
150 g (5½ oz) low fat soft cheese
1 egg
100 g (3½ oz) 0% fat Greek yogurt
50 g (1¾ oz) Parmesan cheese, grated
salt and freshly ground black pepper

1 Heat a large non stick frying pan over a high heat. Add the lamb mince in batches and cook for 5–10 minutes until browned.

2 Meanwhile, warm the olive oil in a large lidded saucepan or lidded flameproof casserole dish over a medium heat. Add the onion and cook for 5–10 minutes until softened.

3 Spoon the mince into the casserole dish or saucepan with the onions. Return the frying pan to the heat and add the wine. Stir well with a wooden spoon to scrape up any pieces from the base of the pan. Boil rapidly for 1 minute, until the wine is slightly reduced, then add the contents of the pan to the casserole dish.

4 Stir the tomatoes, mushrooms, garlic, herbs and spices into the saucepan or casserole dish. Bring to the boil over a high heat then reduce to low, cover, and simmer gently for 1 hour. Remove from the heat. Leave to cool completely then discard the bay leaves.

5 Preheat the oven to Gas Mark 4/180°C/fan oven 160°C. Cut the aubergines lengthways into 5 mm (¼ inch) slices. Spread out over a large non stick baking sheet and bake for 10 minutes or until just softened. Remove from the oven and cover the tray with foil and leave to cool for at least 10 minutes.

6 Spoon one third of the mince mixture into a 32 × 23 cm (12¾ × 9 inch) ovenproof baking dish and spread over the base. Top with half of the aubergine slices then repeat, ending with a third layer of mince.

7 Beat the soft cheese, egg, yogurt, and half of the Parmesan cheese together in a bowl, then season. Spread the topping mixture evenly over the mince and sprinkle with the remaining Parmesan cheese.

8 Bake in the oven for 40 minutes or until golden and bubbling. Remove from the oven and leave to stand for at least 5 minutes before serving.

Serving suggestion
This recipe tastes great with a simple Greek salad made with cucumber, tomatoes, lettuce, olives and feta cheese, remembering to add the extra **ProPoints** values.

Cook's tip
This Greek-inspired bake might take a little time to prepare, but it's well worth the effort. It freezes really well so you could make a large batch and have some ready for another day.

Pork, turkey and chorizo burgers

Victoria Fletcher from Popley, Basingstoke, says this tasty burger recipe is perfect for the weekend when she wants a treat.

✳ Serves 4
26 *ProPoints* values per recipe
45 minutes in total + chilling

30 g (1¼ oz) chorizo, chopped roughly
150 g (5½ oz) boneless pork chop, visible fat removed, and chopped roughly
500 g (1 lb 2 oz) lean turkey mince
1 red pepper, de-seeded and chopped roughly
1 small onion, chopped roughly
1 tablespoon finely chopped fresh basil (or 1 teaspoon dried basil)
salt and freshly ground black pepper

1 Put the chorizo, pork and turkey in a food processor and whizz until smooth, or chop very finely, and place in a large mixing bowl.

2 Put the pepper and onion into the food processor and chop finely (if you don't have a food processor simply chop as finely as possible by hand). Put the mixture in a sieve and leave to drain for 5 minutes to remove any excess moisture.

3 Add the pepper mixture, basil and a generous amount of seasoning to the meats and mix thoroughly until combined. With slightly damp hands, shape the mixture into four even-sized burgers. Put on a plate, cover and chill in the fridge for at least 30 minutes, or for up to 24 hours. Or put them in the freezer for 15 minutes.

4 Preheat the grill or barbecue. Cook the burgers for 8–10 minutes on each side or until thoroughly cooked. There shouldn't be any pink meat and the juices will run clear when a knife is inserted once it is cooked through.

Cook's tip
This recipe can also serve 6 for 4 ***ProPoints*** values per serving.

Creamy bacon pasta

This quick and easy recipe comes from keen cook *Helen Griffin* from Harrogate, North Yorkshire. It's perfect for a midweek dinner as it's filling and tasty.

Serves 2
25 *ProPoints* values per recipe
35 minutes in total

4 rashers lean back bacon
125 g (4½ oz) dried pasta, such as penne or fusilli
calorie controlled cooking spray
1 large onion, diced
2 red or yellow peppers, de-seeded and diced
1 garlic clove, peeled and sliced
1 teaspoon dried Italian herbs
¼ teaspoon smoked paprika
4 slices pickled red jalapeños, drained and chopped
1 vegetable stock cube
100 g (3½ oz) low fat soft cheese
100 g (3½ oz) frozen peas
salt and freshly ground black pepper

1 Preheat the grill to high. Put the bacon on a rack over a grill tray and cook for 2–3 minutes on each side or until cooked through and just starting to colour. Cut into 1 cm (½ inch) pieces and set aside.

2 Bring a large saucepan of water to the boil. Add the pasta and cook according to packet instructions. Drain, reserving 4–6 tablespoons of water.

3 Meanwhile, spray a large non stick frying pan with cooking spray and add the onion, peppers, garlic, herbs, paprika and jalapeños. Cook over a high heat for 3–5 minutes, stirring often, until just starting to soften.

4 Reduce the heat to low. Crumble over the stock cube, add the reserved water from the pasta and stir well until dissolved. Mix in the soft cheese, peas, and some seasoning. Bring to a simmer and cook for a further 4–5 minutes, stirring occasionally, until the peas are tender.

5 Add the pasta to the vegetables and stir to coat in the sauce. Divide between two bowls, sprinkle over the reserved bacon and serve.

Spanish chicken involtini

Leader *Trizia Clarke* from Trinity, Jersey, really enjoys cooking. Her family love this recipe because it's full of flavour, and she loves it because it's so easy to prepare. Rice, potatoes or couscous are ideal to serve with this dish but remember to add the extra *ProPoints* values.

Serves 2
16 *ProPoints* values per recipe
20 minutes preparation + cooling, 40 minutes cooking

100 g (3½ oz) butternut squash, peeled, de-seeded and cut into 1 cm (½ inch) cubes
200 g (7 oz) red pepper, de-seeded and cut into 1 cm (½ inch) cubes
1 teaspoon paprika
calorie controlled cooking spray
60 g (2 oz) ready-to-eat chorizo, diced
2 × 165 g (5¾ oz) skinless boneless chicken breasts
2 tablespoons medium fat soft cheese with sweet chilli
salt and freshly ground black pepper

1 Preheat the oven to Gas Mark 6/200°C/fan oven 180°C. Place the squash and peppers in a large ovenproof dish. Sprinkle over half of the paprika, season and spray with the cooking spray.

2 Bake in the oven for 20 minutes, until tender and starting to colour at the edges. Remove from the oven and mix in the chorizo. Leave to cool completely.

3 Meanwhile, cut the chicken in half lengthways. Place each piece between two sheets of cling film and use a rolling pin or meat mallet to flatten the chicken into four long thin strips. Season.

4 Divide the soft cheese between the chicken strips, spreading it neatly over the top of each one. Top with the squash mixture. Roll each strip up tightly and secure with two cocktail sticks each.

5 Spray an ovenproof baking dish with the cooking spray then place the chicken and any remaining filling in the dish. Sprinkle over the remaining paprika and spray again.

6 Bake in the oven, uncovered, for 15–20 minutes or until cooked through.

7 Remove the cocktail sticks and serve.

Curried chicken bake

Having been reunited with the love of her life after 30 years, *Helen Solomon* from Kinver, Stourbridge, is determined to lose weight for the last time. This is one of her favourite cauliflower dishes.

Serves 4
26 ProPoints values per recipe
55 minutes in total

1 large **cauliflower**, *cut into florets*
1 large head of **broccoli**, *cut into florets*
calorie controlled cooking spray
450 g (1 lb) **skinless boneless chicken breasts**,
   cut into chunks
1 **onion**, *diced*
2 tablespoons medium curry powder
2 tablespoons plain flour
600 ml (20 fl oz) **skimmed milk**
40 g (1½ oz) half fat cheese, grated coarsely
salt and freshly ground black pepper

1 Preheat the oven to Gas Mark 5/190°C/fan oven 170°C. Bring a large saucepan of water to the boil. Add the cauliflower and broccoli, bring back to the boil and cook for 3–4 minutes until just tender. Drain and leave to cool in the colander.

2 Meanwhile, spray a large non stick frying pan with cooking spray and warm over a high heat. Add the chicken and cook for 5–10 minutes, turning occasionally, until golden. Remove from the pan and set aside. Return the pan to the heat and spray with more cooking spray. Add the onion and cook for 5 minutes, stirring often, until softened and starting to colour.

3 Reduce the heat to low and mix in the curry powder and flour. Gradually add the milk, stirring continuously until smooth. Bring to the boil and simmer for 5 minutes until slightly thickened. Add the cooled cauliflower, broccoli and chicken and turn in the sauce to coat.

4 Spray a 23 × 30 cm (9 × 12 inch) ovenproof baking dish with cooking spray. Spoon the cauliflower mixture into the dish and arrange neatly. Sprinkle over the grated cheese and bake in the oven for 10 minutes or until golden and bubbling. Serve immediately.

Chorizo tagliatelle

Gold Member *Karen Shepherd* from Chesterfield in Derbyshire chose this filling dish because it's simple to make for one person. It's good with other zero **ProPoints** value roast vegetables too, such as **leeks** and **peppers**.

Serves 1
10 ProPoints values per recipe
45 minutes in total

125 g (4½ oz) **carrot**, *peeled and cut into*
   1–2 cm cubes
250 g (9 oz) **butternut squash**, *peeled,*
   de-seeded and cut into 1–2 cm cubes
calorie controlled cooking spray
30 g (1¼ oz) chorizo, diced
1 small **onion**, *diced*
150 g (5½ oz) **mushrooms**, *sliced*
227 g tin chopped **tomatoes**
100 ml (3½ fl oz) vegetable stock
½ teaspoon dried Italian herbs
75 g (2¾ oz) frozen **peas**
40 g (1½ oz) dried tagliatelle
50 g (1¾ oz) medium-fat soft cheese with
   sun-dried tomato and basil
a handful of **fresh basil** leaves, to garnish

1 Preheat the oven to Gas Mark 4/180°C/fan oven 160°C. Bring a small pan of water to the boil. Add the carrots, return to the boil and cook for 3 minutes until just tender. Drain.

2 Put the carrot and squash in a medium roasting tin. Spray with cooking spray and then bake for 30 minutes until softened and starting to colour.

3 Meanwhile, warm a large non stick frying pan over a medium heat. Add the chorizo and cook for 2 minutes or until its orangey oils are released. Add the onion and mushrooms and cook for a further 5 minutes, stirring often, until coated in the chorizo oil and starting to soften.

4 Stir in the tomatoes, stock, herbs and peas. Bring to the boil then simmer gently for 5 minutes until slightly thickened. Stir in the roasted vegetables and season.

5 Meanwhile, bring a pan of water to the boil and cook the pasta according to packet instructions until tender. Drain. Add the pasta to the tomato sauce along with the soft cheese. Toss everything together and serve garnished with basil leaves.

Tortilla lasagne

This fantastic variation on an Italian classic from *Samantha Smith* of Kettering is ideal if someone in your family isn't keen on pasta.

Serves 4

39 *ProPoints* values per recipe

40 minutes preparation + resting, 35 minutes cooking

calorie controlled cooking spray
1 large onion, diced
1 garlic clove, peeled and crushed
3 rashers lean back bacon, rind removed,
    and cut into strips
100 g (3½ oz) mushrooms, sliced
200 g (7 oz) extra lean beef mince
2 × 400 g cans chopped tomatoes
1 large carrot, peeled and grated coarsely
2 celery sticks, trimmed and grated coarsely
3 flour tortillas (approx. 200 g/7 oz)
175 ml (6 fl oz) reduced fat single cream
150 g (5½ oz) low fat soft cheese
salt and freshly ground black pepper

1 Preheat the oven to Gas Mark 5/190°C/fan oven 170°C. Spray a large non stick frying pan with cooking spray and warm over a high heat. Add the onion and garlic and stir-fry for 5 minutes or until softened. Remove from the pan and set aside.

2 Return the pan to the heat, add the bacon and mushrooms and fry, stirring, until softened and starting to colour. Crumble in the mince and cook for 5–10 minutes until browned, breaking up any large lumps as it cooks.

3 Return the onion to the pan, followed by the tomatoes, carrot and celery. Season and stir well. Reduce the heat and simmer for 10 minutes until thickened.

4 Spoon a third of the meat sauce over the base of an 18 × 24 cm (7 × 9½ inch) ovenproof baking dish. Top with one of the tortillas. Repeat twice more, ending with a tortilla.

5 Warm the cream in a small saucepan over a medium heat. Add the soft cheese and stir until melted, then pour evenly over the tortilla. Bake in the oven for 35 minutes or until golden and bubbling. Remove and leave to rest for 5 minutes before serving.

Roast in a bag

Paula Ewins from Clevedon says this is very quick and versatile, not to mention tasty. It's ideal for caravan holidays as it can be cooked in the oven or in a slow cooker, adjusting your cooking times accordingly.

Serves 1

9 *ProPoints* values per recipe

10 minutes preparation + resting, 35 minutes cooking

150 g (5½ oz) skinless boneless chicken breast
150 g (5½ oz) new potatoes, scrubbed and halved
125 g (4½ oz) carrots, peeled and sliced
100 g (3½ oz) broccoli, cut into florets
1 x 39 g (1½ oz) Weight Watchers Premium Pork sausage
1 bay leaf
2 teaspoons gravy granules
100 ml (3½ fl oz) boiling water
salt and freshly ground black pepper

1 Preheat the oven to Gas Mark 5/190°C/fan oven 170°C. Season the chicken.

2 Place the potatoes, carrots and broccoli in a large roasting bag, top with the chicken and sausage then add the bay leaf.

3 Put the gravy granules in a small jug and add the boiling water. Stir until smooth then pour into the roasting bag. Seal the bag with the tie provided or according to the instructions and put in an ovenproof roasting dish.

4 Roast for 30–35 minutes or until the chicken and sausage are cooked through. Remove from the oven and leave to rest for 3–5 minutes before carefully opening the bag. Discard the bay leaf and serve immediately.

V Try this

For a vegetarian alternative, replace the chicken with a Quorn fillet, the sausage with a vegetarian sausage and the gravy granules with vegetarian gravy granules, for 7 ***ProPoints*** values per serving.

Cook's tip

Roasting bags are available from all major supermarkets and you'll find them beside the foil and cling film.

This easy all-in-one roast is quick to prepare and there isn't even any washing up. The chicken cooks with the gravy, which adds lots of flavour and makes it so moist.

Bolognese burgers

This modern take on 'burger and chips' is a favourite of *Deborah Sunter*, from Bradford, West Yorkshire. It's quick and easy to prepare and very filling. She hopes other Members enjoy this recipe as much as her family does.

❋ (Burgers only) Serves 4
34 *ProPoints* values per recipe
40 minutes in total

400 g (14 oz) **potatoes** *(such as Maris Piper),*
    cut into thick wedges
1 tablespoon olive oil
3 teaspoons dried Italian herbs
450 g (1 lb) extra lean beef mince
2 tablespoons tomato purée
½ teaspoon chilli powder, or to taste
1 small **onion***, chopped finely*
salt and freshly ground black pepper

1 Preheat the oven to Gas Mark 6/200°C/fan oven 180°C. Put the potato wedges in a large bowl with the oil, 2 teaspoons of the Italian herbs and some seasoning. Mix well until coated.

2 Spread the wedges out in a single layer on a large non stick baking tray. Bake in the oven for 30 minutes, turning once during cooking, until tender and golden.

3 Meanwhile, put the mince, remaining herbs, tomato purée, chilli powder, onion and a pinch of seasoning in a large bowl. Mix together until well combined. With damp hands, divide the mixture into four and shape into even-sized burgers.

4 Preheat the grill to medium-high or heat the barbecue. Cook the burgers for 7–8 minutes on each side or until cooked to your liking. Remove the wedges from the oven and put on kitchen paper to remove any excess oil. Serve the burgers with the wedges.

Try this

Use Italian ingredients such as **rocket**, **fresh basil** leaves, and finely sliced **fennel** to give a real lift to your salads.

Summer risotto with trout

Ingrid House from Rotherham is lucky enough to have a constant supply of trout from a friend and is always looking for different ways to cook it. She says she is slowly but surely losing weight with the support of her Leader, Sarah Padley.

Serves 2
19 *ProPoints* values per recipe
40 minutes in total

500 ml (18 fl oz) vegetable stock
100 g (3½ oz) **mushrooms***, cleaned and sliced*
125 g (4½ oz) **green beans***, trimmed and cut into 3 cm*
    (1¼ inch) pieces
calorie controlled cooking spray
1 **onion***, diced*
2 large **garlic cloves***, sliced thinly*
1 tablespoon chopped **fresh dill***, plus extra to serve*
125 g (4½ oz) dried risotto rice
4 tablespoons dry white wine
150 g (5½ oz) **poached trout***, flaked into bite-sized pieces*
salt and freshly ground black pepper

1 Put the stock in a large saucepan and bring to the boil over a high heat. Add the mushrooms and beans and bring back to the boil. Reduce the heat to low and cook for 2 minutes then remove the mushrooms and beans with a slotted spoon and set aside. Keep the stock warm.

2 Spray a saucepan with cooking spray and warm over a high heat. Add the onion and cook for 5 minutes, stirring often until softened and starting to colour. Mix in the garlic and dill and continue cooking for a further minute.

3 Reduce the heat to low. Stir in the rice and cook for 1 minute. Add the wine and continue stirring until all the liquid has been absorbed. Add a ladleful of the hot stock and stir until all the liquid has been absorbed. Continue doing this for about 20 minutes, until all the stock has been used and the rice is tender.

4 Fold the reserved mushrooms, green beans, trout and some seasoning into the rice and cook for 1–2 minutes until piping hot. Garnish with more dill and serve.

Venison sausage casserole

Christine Owen from Woburn Sands, Milton Keynes, enjoys cooking from scratch. Her warming dish caters for the whole family.

❄ Serves 2

16 *ProPoints* values per recipe

30 minutes preparation, 30 minutes cooking

calorie controlled cooking spray
200 g (7 oz) venison sausages (about 4 sausages)
125 g (4½ oz) **shallots**, peeled
1 **garlic clove**, crushed
175 ml (6 fl oz) red wine
20 g (¾ oz) redcurrant jelly
2 bay leaves
4 **fresh thyme** sprigs
250 ml (9 fl oz) beef stock, made with half a stock cube
400 g (14 oz) **celeriac**, peeled and chopped
100 g (3½ oz) **Quark**
2 tablespoons chopped **fresh chives**
200 g (7 oz) fine **green beans**, trimmed
3 teaspoons instant gravy granules
salt and freshly ground black pepper

1 Spray a 1.5 litre (2¾ pint) flameproof casserole dish with cooking spray. Place over a medium heat and add the sausages, cooking them gently until browned. Lift out and set aside.

2 Add the shallots and garlic to the casserole and cook gently until browned. Return the sausages and add the wine, redcurrant jelly, bay leaves and thyme. Pour in the stock, cover and gently simmer for 30 minutes.

3 Meanwhile, bring a saucepan of water to the boil, add the celeriac and cook for 25 minutes, or until tender. Drain. Using a food processor or a hand-held blender, whizz the celeriac until smooth. Add the Quark and blend until creamy. Stir in the chives and season.

4 Bring another saucepan of water to the boil, add the beans and cook for 5–6 minutes.

5 When the casserole is ready, discard the bay leaves and thyme. Lift the sausages and shallots on to a warmed dish, then boil the stock, adding the gravy granules to thicken it. Return the sausages and shallots to the casserole and stir well. Serve with the celeriac and beans.

Creamy chicken with three mustards

Kate Thompson from Chadsmoor, Cannnock, loves this recipe as it's real comfort food, quick to prepare and the family loves it.

❄ Serves 4

41 *ProPoints* values per recipe

40 minutes in total

calorie controlled cooking spray
1 **onion**, chopped finely
250 g (9 oz) **mushrooms**, sliced
450 g (1 lb) **skinless boneless chicken breasts**, diced
200 g (7 oz) dried long grain white rice
250 ml (9 fl oz) dry white wine
200 g (7 oz) Weight Watchers crème fraîche
1 teaspoon Dijon mustard
1 teaspoon wholegrain mustard
1 teaspoon English mustard
200 ml (7 fl oz) chicken stock
salt and freshly ground black pepper

1 Heat a large non stick frying pan and spray with cooking spray. Add the onion and mushrooms and cook over a medium heat for 5–7 minutes until softened, but not too brown.

2 Add the chicken and cook until browned. Meanwhile, bring a saucepan of water to the boil, add the rice and cook according to the packet instructions.

3 Turning the heat up to high under the frying pan, add the white wine to the chicken and bubble vigorously until reduced by half and you can no longer smell the alcohol.

4 Mix together the crème fraîche and mustards and stir into the chicken. Add the stock, then simmer gently for 7–8 minutes until the chicken is cooked through. Season, then serve with the rice.

Try this
This dish is equally good with pasta instead of rice, for the same *ProPoints* values, or serve with some zero *ProPoints* value **vegetables**, reducing the *ProPoints* values to 6 per serving.

Stuffed butternut squash with Quorn

Butternut squash is a real favourite of *Helen Warner* from Farlington, Portsmouth, and this recipe uses it brilliantly. Helen says you can use goat's cheese instead of feta, but make sure you adjust the **ProPoints** values.

V Serves 2
9 ProPoints values per recipe
40 minutes preparation, 1 hour cooking

1 **butternut squash** (approx. 400 g/14 oz)
2 teaspoons olive oil
½ teaspoon chilli flakes
1 teaspoon dried rosemary
1 **garlic clove**, crushed
calorie controlled cooking spray
1 **onion**, chopped
1 red **pepper**, de-seeded and chopped
1 **courgette**, chopped
100 g (3½ oz) **Quorn mince**
400 g can chopped **tomatoes**
50 g (1¾ oz) feta cheese
freshly ground black pepper
a handful of **fresh parsley** sprigs, to garnish

1 Preheat the oven to Gas Mark 4/180°C/fan oven 160°C.

2 Cut the butternut squash in half lengthways, scoop out and discard the seeds. Put in a large roasting tin. Mix together the olive oil, chilli, rosemary and garlic and brush all over the top of the squash. Bake for around 1 hour or until tender.

3 Meanwhile, make the filling. Spray a large non stick frying pan with cooking spray and cook the onion for 5 minutes until softened. Add the pepper and courgette and continue to cook for 5 minutes.

4 Add the mince and chopped tomatoes and simmer for 10 minutes. Once the squash is cooked, spoon the mince mixture on to each half and crumble the feta cheese on top. Season, return to the oven and cook for 10 minutes until the cheese is just starting to turn golden. Serve, garnished with parsley sprigs.

Turkey stroganoff

Margaret Molloy from Ormskirk in Lancashire thought up this recipe after rejoining Weight Watchers. Her family just loves it and she hopes yours will too. It's delicious served with fine green beans and 150 g (5½ oz) new potatoes per person for a further 3 *ProPoints* values per serving.

Serves 4
18 ProPoints values per recipe
40 minutes in total

calorie controlled cooking spray
500 g (1 lb 2 oz) skinless boneless turkey breasts,
    cut into strips
1 onion, chopped finely
200 g (7 oz) mushrooms, sliced
2 garlic cloves, crushed
600 ml (20 fl oz) chicken stock
3 tablespoons reduced fat crème fraîche
4 teaspoons French mustard
1–2 teaspoons dried tarragon
salt and freshly ground black pepper

1 Lightly spray a large non stick frying pan with the cooking spray. Add the turkey strips and cook over a medium-high heat until browned. Add the onion, mushrooms and garlic and cook for 4–5 minutes until the onion is soft.

2 Add the stock and simmer for 10 minutes.

3 Stir in the crème fraîche, mustard and tarragon. Increase the heat and allow the sauce to reduce and thicken slightly. Season to taste and cook over a low heat for a further 10 minutes. Serve immediately.

Cook's tip
Tarragon is a very aromatic herb, so add 1 teaspoon first, then if you'd like a more pronounced flavour, add a little extra.

Venison in red wine

This recipe is often enjoyed by *Tara Breckell's* family, in Tupton in the West Midlands. If you want a smoother sauce, Tara suggests running it through a sieve before serving. Serve with tenderstem broccoli.

Serves 2
21 ProPoints values per recipe
50 minutes in total

1 tablespoon olive oil
200 g (7 oz) potatoes, peeled and chopped
2 garlic cloves, crushed
½ teaspoon dried rosemary
calorie controlled cooking spray
2 × 120 g (4½ oz) venison haunch steaks
1 shallot, chopped finely
125 ml (4 fl oz) red wine
1 tablespoon redcurrant jelly
200 ml (7 fl oz) beef stock
1 heaped teaspoon cornflour, blended with
    1 tablespoon cold water
salt and freshly ground black pepper

1 Preheat the oven to Gas Mark 6/200°C/fan oven 180°C.

2 Heat the oil in a non stick frying pan and add the potatoes, half the garlic and the rosemary. Stir and cook the potatoes for about 5 minutes. Transfer to a baking tray. Bake for 20 minutes, turning once or twice.

3 Wipe out the pan with kitchen paper, spray with the cooking spray and add the venison steaks, cooking them over a medium-high heat for 5 minutes on each side. Remove and keep warm, covered with foil.

4 Add the remaining garlic and shallot to the frying pan and cook over a medium heat for 3 minutes, then add the wine and allow it to bubble up until the liquid has reduced by one third. Add the redcurrant jelly and stock and bubble rapidly for 3–4 minutes. Season to taste. Turn down the heat and add the blended cornflour, stirring until thickened.

5 Meanwhile, in a saucepan, bring a small amount of water to the boil and steam the broccoli. Return the venison to the sauce and cook for a further 5 minutes.

6 Lift the venison steaks on to warmed plates, allowing them to rest for 2 minutes. Serve with the potatoes and sauce.

Pasta-less lasagne

Dee Dee McCollin from London loves the idea of lasagne, but not the high **ProPoints** values that often go with it. Using courgettes and aubergines instead of pasta keeps this filling dish low in **ProPoints** values.

❋ Serves 6
42 ProPoints values per recipe
40 minutes preparation + resting, 40 minutes cooking

4 large courgettes, *sliced thinly lengthways*
3 large aubergines, *sliced thinly lengthways*
1 tablespoon olive oil
2 onions, *chopped*
5 garlic cloves, *crushed*
1 red pepper, *de-seeded and chopped*
1 green or yellow pepper, *de-seeded and chopped*
500 g (1 lb 2 oz) turkey mince
2 beef tomatoes, *chopped*
100 g (3½ oz) tomato purée
1 teaspoon dried thyme
1 tablespoon dried oregano
1 tablespoon chopped fresh basil
salt and freshly ground black pepper
For the white sauce
600 ml (20 fl oz) skimmed milk
1 small onion, *chopped roughly*
1 bay leaf
1 tablespoon olive oil
2 tablespoons plain flour
75 g (2¾ oz) low fat Cheddar cheese, grated

1 Preheat the grill to medium. Arrange the courgette and aubergine slices on the grill rack and grill on both sides until lightly browned. Set aside.

2 Preheat the oven to Gas Mark 6/200°C/fan oven 180°C.

3 Heat 1 tablespoon of olive oil in a large non stick frying pan and fry the onions, garlic and peppers until softened. Add the turkey mince and cook until browned. Stir in the tomatoes, tomato purée, herbs and seasoning and cook for a further 5–8 minutes.

4 Meanwhile, to make the white sauce, put the milk, onion and bay leaf in a saucepan and heat until almost boiling. Set aside to cool.

5 In a separate lidded saucepan, heat the oil and stir in the flour. Cook over a low heat for 1 minute. Strain the cooled milk to remove the onion and bay leaf, then add a little at a time to the flour mixture, stirring until smooth. Heat until thickened, stirring constantly. Remove from the heat.

6 Place the courgettes over the base of a 3 litre (5¼ pint) baking dish. Add the turkey mixture, then layer the aubergines on top, making sure that all the turkey mixture is covered. Pour the white sauce over the aubergines and sprinkle the cheese over the surface.

7 Cook on the middle shelf of the oven for 40 minutes. Allow the dish to sit for 10 minutes before serving.

Try this
You can use extra lean beef mince instead of turkey mince if you prefer, for 8 **ProPoints** values per serving, or use frozen Quorn mince to make a vegetarian version for 6 **ProPoints** values per serving. You could also omit the cheese to reduce the **ProPoints** values per serving.

Cook's tip
To prevent lumps, use a silicone-coated whisk when making the white sauce.

Feed a crowd with this amazing lasagne, made with layers of vegetables and turkey mince instead of pasta. The portions are incredibly generous and everyone will be impressed.

Guilt-free ratatouille

Mum of two *Karen Rushmer* from Bishopsgate in Norwich says this recipe makes either a great main meal for four or a starter for six. It also freezes well so why not make a big batch and put some in the freezer?

V ❄ Serves 4
9 ProPoints values per recipe
35 minutes preparation, 25 minutes cooking

2 tablespoons olive oil
1 large onion, sliced
3 garlic cloves, crushed
1 butternut squash, peeled, de-seeded and chopped
2 × 400 g cans chopped tomatoes
2 tablespoons dried Italian mixed herbs
4 bay leaves
2 courgettes, sliced
8 mushrooms, chopped
a kettleful of boiling water
2 handfuls of spinach
salt and freshly ground black pepper

1 Heat the oil in a large lidded saucepan and fry the onion for about 10 minutes until softened. Add the garlic and cook for 1 minute. Season.

2 Add the butternut squash and tomatoes and give everything a good stir to mix it all together. Cover and simmer for 10 minutes.

3 Add the herbs and bay leaves and continue to simmer for 2 minutes. Add the courgettes and mushrooms and stir in. Pour over 300 ml (10 fl oz) boiling water, season well then cover and simmer for 25 minutes, checking the fluid level occasionally, adding some water if it starts to stick.

4 A couple of minutes before the end of cooking, stir in the spinach. Pick out and discard the bay leaves, then serve.

Cook's tip
Store any leftover ratatouille in an airtight container in the fridge for up to 3 days.

Thai Quorn red curry

Bryher Hill from St Mellons in Cardiff reached her goal in 2009 and went on to join the '100 lb Club'. She loves using Quorn in this recipe as its low **ProPoints** values mean she can enjoy a delicious curry like this made with coconut milk.

V Serves 2
24 ProPoints values per recipe
40 minutes in total

calorie controlled cooking spray
1 large onion, diced
100 g (3½ oz) baby corn, sliced
1 red pepper, de-seeded and sliced
150 g (5½ oz) Quorn chicken-style pieces
2 teaspoons Thai red curry paste
200 ml (7 fl oz) light coconut milk
2 pak choi, sliced
200 g (7 oz) beansprouts
a kettleful of boiling water
75 g (2¾ oz) dried egg noodles

1 Spray a large wok with the cooking spray and fry the onion, baby corn, pepper and Quorn in the pan for 5–10 minutes until it starts to soften.

2 Stir in the curry paste, then add the coconut milk and mix everything together well. Reduce the heat to a simmer. Add the pak choi and beansprouts and 100 ml (3½ oz) boiling water and simmer for 5–10 minutes.

3 Meanwhile, bring a saucepan of water to the boil and cook the noodles according to the packet instructions.

4 Divide the noodles between two bowls and spoon over the curry.

Try this
Serve with a squeeze of lime and some chopped fresh coriander on top for no extra **ProPoints** values.

Cod with pesto and cheese topping

Gold Member *Joanne Ninnes* from Whirlow in Sheffield first joined Weight Watchers 25 years ago. She developed this delicious recipe as she loves how well the cheesy flavour goes with the fish. And adding lots of lovely vegetables makes this dish extra filling and tasty.

Serves 4
21 *ProPoints* values per recipe
25 minutes preparation, 25 minutes cooking

2 teaspoons olive oil
1 onion, sliced finely
175 g (6 oz) mushrooms, sliced finely
1 courgette, chopped finely
400 g can chopped tomatoes
1 tablespoon pesto
675 g (1 lb 8 oz) skinless cod fillet
50 g (1¾ oz) half fat Cheddar cheese, grated
salt and freshly ground black pepper

1 Preheat the oven to Gas Mark 4/180°C/fan oven 160°C. Heat the olive oil in a large flameproof casserole dish and fry the onion over a medium heat for 5 minutes until softened.

2 Add the mushrooms and courgette and continue to cook for another 5 minutes, stirring every now and then, until the vegetables are soft.

3 Pour in the chopped tomatoes, add the pesto and stir into the vegetables. Continue to cook over a medium heat for 5 minutes until the sauce has thickened.

4 Place the fish in a 2 litre (3½ pint) ovenproof dish. Spoon over the vegetable and pesto mixture to cover the fish. Sprinkle the cheese evenly over the top.

5 Cook in the oven for 25 minutes until the fish is cooked and the cheese is melted and golden.

Prawn saganaki

Retired teacher *Tony Burrows* from West Kirby, Wirral, adapted this popular Greek meal to make a lower **ProPoints** value version. Succulent prawns combined with a Mediterranean-style sauce are perfect hot and straight from the oven, or warm with a crisp salad.

Serves 2
22 ProPoints values per recipe
20 minutes preparation, 40 minutes cooking

calorie controlled cooking spray
1 onion, chopped finely
½ red or green pepper, de-seeded and chopped
1 garlic clove, crushed
400 g (14 oz) large tomatoes, skinned and chopped,
    or 400 g can chopped tomatoes
250 ml (9 fl oz) dry white wine
2 tablespoons chopped fresh parsley
½ teaspoon granular sweetener
1 tablespoon olive oil
200 g (7 oz) raw king prawns, peeled
100 g (3½ oz) feta cheese, crumbled

1 Preheat the oven to Gas Mark 4/180°C/fan oven 160°C.

2 Heat a large, lidded, non stick saucepan and spray with cooking spray. Add the onion and then cook for 10 minutes until softened and golden. Add the pepper, garlic, tomatoes, wine, parsley, sweetener and olive oil. Cover and bring to the boil, then uncover and simmer for 20–30 minutes until thickened.

3 Stir in the prawns and cook for 2–3 minutes until the prawns have turned from grey to pink and have cooked through. Spoon into a small ovenproof casserole dish and sprinkle with the feta cheese. Cook in the oven for 5 minutes to soften the cheese and then serve.

Sausage, apple and ginger casserole

Not only is this recipe ideal for the family, it's perfect for the middle of the week and easy on the pocket as well. *Anne Stubbs* from Saltburn in Cleveland says that using firm, unpeeled eating apples works best.

Serves 4
16 ProPoints values per recipe
20 minutes preparation, 1 hour 5 minutes cooking

8 x 39 g (1½ oz) Weight Watchers Premium Pork Sausages
1 onion, sliced
1 red pepper, de-seeded and sliced
1 parsnip, chopped
1 apple, cored and sliced
600 ml (20 fl oz) fiery diet ginger beer
1 cm (½ inch) fresh root ginger, grated
2 teaspoons dried rosemary
1 chicken stock cube, dissolved in 4 tablespoons
    boiling water
1 tablespoon cornflour
freshly ground black pepper

1 Preheat the oven to Gas Mark 6/200°C/fan oven 180°C.

2 Prick the sausages all over and dry-fry in a large, lidded, flameproof and ovenproof casserole dish until golden all over. Remove the sausages and set aside.

3 Add the onion, pepper and parsnip to the casserole dish and cook for 5 minutes until starting to turn golden.

4 Return the sausages to the dish with the apple. Mix together the ginger beer, ginger, rosemary and stock and pour into the dish, then season. Bring to the boil, cover and transfer to the oven for 1 hour.

5 Mix the cornflour with a little water and stir until smooth then add to the casserole. Return to the oven for 5 minutes until the sauce thickens, then serve.

Jacqui's turkey curry

Helen Emery, from Winchester in Hampshire, was originally given this recipe by her mother-in-law Jacqui. After joining Weight Watchers, she adapted it to make this delicious, lower *ProPoints* value version. Helen recommends varying the quantities of the spices, depending on personal taste.

Serves 4
42 ProPoints values per recipe
40 minutes in total

calorie controlled cooking spray
2 onions, sliced
2 teaspoons ground ginger
1 teaspoon ground turmeric
2 teaspoons ground fenugreek
2 teaspoons garam masala
½–1 teaspoon ground chilli
600 g (1 lb 5 oz) turkey mince
2 red or green peppers, de-seeded and sliced
300 ml (10 fl oz) passata
200 g can creamed mushrooms
285 g can sliced mushrooms
150 g (5½ oz) dried basmati rice
225 g (8 oz) spinach

1 Heat a large, lidded non stick frying pan and spray with cooking spray. Add the onions and cook for 5 minutes, until starting to colour and soften.

2 Add the spices and cook for 1 minute. Add a splash of water if the mixture starts to stick.

3 Add the turkey mince in batches, breaking it up with a wooden spoon. Once the mince has sealed and browned, add the peppers and cook for 2–3 minutes.

4 Stir in the passata, creamed mushrooms and sliced mushrooms. Cover the pan, reduce the heat to a simmer and cook for 15 minutes.

5 Meanwhile, bring a saucepan of water to the boil, add the rice and cook according to packet instructions, then drain.

6 About 3–4 minutes before the curry is ready, add the spinach, stirring it through until it has wilted.

7 Share the rice between four warmed serving bowls. Spoon the curry on top and serve at once.

Tray-baked plaice with spinach and olives

Richard Gaunt from Upton, Wirral, sums up his experience with Weight Watchers as 'amazing' – he's lost 2 stone and now feels confident in everything he does. Richard loves fish and chose this recipe to show that a tomato sauce is just as tasty as a creamy one.

Serves 4
29 ProPoints values per recipe
20 minutes preparation, 15 minutes cooking

3 teaspoons olive oil
2 garlic cloves, sliced
125 ml (4 fl oz) dry white wine, such as Chardonnay
2 × 400 g cans plum tomatoes
100 g jar anchovy fillets, reserving 2 teaspoons of the oil, then fillets patted dry with kitchen paper
150 g (5½ oz) pitted black olives, chopped finely
25 g (1 oz) fresh basil, torn roughly
4 x 125 g (4½ oz) extra-trimmed plaice fillets (but not necessarily skinned)
4 fresh rosemary twigs (optional)
150 g (5½ oz) spinach
freshly ground black pepper

1 Preheat the oven to Gas Mark 6/200°C/fan oven 180°C.

2 Place a medium saucepan over a medium heat and add 2 teaspoons of oil. Heat gently and add the garlic. Cook the garlic until softened, but not browned, and add the wine to the pan. Cook for 1 minute, then add the tomatoes, breaking them down with the back of a spoon. Lower the heat to a simmer and season.

3 Mix together the anchovies, olives and basil and then mix with the reserved oil to make a spreadable paste.

4 Lay the plaice fillets, skin-side up, on a board and season. Spread the paste equally over the fillets to cover them. Roll up each fillet from the narrow end and secure with the rosemary twigs, if using, or cocktail sticks.

5 Spoon the sauce into a shallow flameproof and ovenproof dish and place the fish on top. Drizzle with the remaining oil and cook in the oven for 15 minutes.

6 Lift the fish on to warmed plates and return the pan to a medium heat. Add the spinach and allow it to wilt for 1 minute. Spoon around the fish and serve.

This fabulous fish dish looks stylish and tastes divine. It's a good one to make if you have friends for supper not only because it tastes great but because it cooks so quickly in the oven too.

Fish benachin

Assistant head teacher *Tina Davey* from Cwmbran in South Wales was inspired to create this dish following a trip to Gambia. A true 'benachin' is a one pot meal, but Tina has adapted this recipe to cook on a hob rather than an open fire.

Serves 4
43 *ProPoints* values per recipe
30 minutes preparation + 30 minutes marinating,
30 minutes cooking

4 × 150 g (5½ oz) white fish *fillets such as* cod *or* haddock
juice of 1½ limes
calorie controlled cooking spray
1 onion*, sliced*
400 g can chopped tomatoes
1 aubergine*, diced*
1 butternut squash*, peeled, de-seeded and diced*
a kettleful of boiling water
300 g (10½ oz) dried brown rice
1 chicken stock cube
5 fresh parsley *sprigs, chopped finely*
25 g (1 oz) fresh chives*, chopped finely*
freshly ground black pepper

1 Place the fish in a non-metallic dish and pour over the lime juice. Season and set aside to marinate for 30 minutes.

2 Heat a large lidded saucepan and spray with the cooking spray. Cook the onion for 10 minutes until starting to turn golden. Add the tomatoes, aubergine and squash and 400 ml (14 fl oz) boiling water. Season, bring to the boil, then cover. Simmer for 20 minutes. Meanwhile, bring a saucepan of water to the boil and cook the rice according to the packet instructions.

3 Bring a small amount of water to a very gentle simmer in a shallow saucepan and poach the fish for 6–8 minutes, depending on its thickness. Crumble half of the stock cube into a bowl and stir in the herbs.

4 Stir the remaining stock cube into the tomato and vegetable stew. Carefully lift the fish on to the stew, then sprinkle with the herb mixture. Cover the pan and cook for 5–10 minutes. Serve with the rice.

Creamy hazelnut pasta

For *Diane Pullen* from South Godstone, Surrey, Weight Watchers is the only plan that works for her. She chose this recipe because it's fast and slightly different to the usual pasta dish.

V Serves 4
40 *ProPoints* values per recipe
30 minutes in total

calorie controlled cooking spray
1 small onion*, chopped finely*
1 garlic clove*, crushed*
2 small courgettes*, halved lengthways, then sliced*
4 mushrooms*, quartered*
300 g (10½ oz) dried spaghetti
15 g (½ oz) hazelnuts, toasted (see Cook's tip) and chopped
200 g (7 oz) low fat soft cheese
freshly ground black pepper
a handful of fresh basil *leaves, to garnish*

1 Spray a non stick frying pan with the cooking spray. Add the onion, garlic, courgettes and mushrooms and cook for 10–15 minutes until starting to turn golden.

2 Meanwhile, bring a large pan of water to the boil and cook the spaghetti according to the packet instructions. Drain well and return to the pan.

3 Add the hazelnuts and soft cheese to the pan and stir to coat all the ingredients, taking care not to let the cheese melt too much. Add to the drained spaghetti and serve, scattered with basil leaves.

Cook's tips

In addition to using basil for garnishing, stir in a couple of torn fresh basil leaves at the end for an extra boost of flavour for no extra ***ProPoints*** values.

To toast hazelnuts, preheat the oven to Gas Mark 6/200°C/fan oven 180°C. Put the hazelnuts in a baking tray with high sides and roast until browned, checking regularly to make sure they don't burn. Remove the toasted nuts from the oven and put into a wire sieve. Shake the sieve to loosen the skins from the nuts and then pick out the nuts which are free from their skins.

Thyme-scented pork with creamy green veg

Lindsey Patterson from Bury St Edmunds says that using a roasting bag to cook the pork keeps the meat tender and low in **ProPoints** values.

Serves 2
11 ProPoints values per recipe
1 hour 15 minutes in total

½ small **butternut squash**, *peeled, de-seeded and sliced thinly*
1 large **onion**, *sliced thinly*
2 **garlic cloves**, *sliced thinly*
a small bunch of **fresh thyme**, *stalks discarded*
1 chicken stock cube
200 g (7 oz) **pork tenderloin**
freshly ground black pepper
For the creamy vegetables
1 chicken stock cube
1 **celery heart**, *sliced*
1 bunch of **asparagus**, *trimmed and chopped*
125 g (4½ oz) frozen **peas**
50 g (1¾ oz) low fat soft cheese

1 Preheat the oven to Gas Mark 1/140°C/fan oven 120°C.

2 Put the squash, onion and garlic in an oven roasting bag, then put the thyme on top. Crush the stock cube and sprinkle over the pork, then put this on top of the squash and season. Secure the bag with the tie provided.

3 Put the bag in a roasting tin and cook in the oven for 1 hour.

4 After 30 minutes, prepare the rest of the vegetables. Dissolve the stock cube in a lidded pan with 300 ml (10 fl oz) boiling water. Bring to a gentle simmer and add the celery. Cover and braise for 20 minutes.

5 Uncover the pan and add the asparagus, reserving the tips for later. Continue to simmer, uncovered, for 10 minutes, allowing the cooking liquid to gradually reduce.

6 Stir in the asparagus tips and peas and cook for about 3 more minutes. Stir in the cream cheese to melt through and season.

7 Slice the pork and serve with the squash and the creamy green vegetables.

Smoked haddock and bacon pasta bake

Sheila Thomson from Hawick in Scotland loves smoked fish and she adapted this pasta bake from a recipe she discovered over 20 years ago when on holiday in Oban.

Serves 4
39 ProPoints values per recipe
50 minutes preparation, 25 minutes cooking

4 rashers lean back bacon, *trimmed of visible fat*
150g (5½ oz) dried **wholewheat pasta**, *such as penne*
200 ml (7 fl oz) **skimmed milk**
450 g (1 lb) skinless **smoked haddock** *(dyed or undyed)*
3 tablespoons half-fat crème fraîche
2 **eggs**
2 teaspoons Dijon mustard
40 g (1½ oz) Weight Watchers cheese or reduced-fat cheese, *grated*
40 g (1½ oz) slice wholemeal bread
2 plum **tomatoes**, *sliced thinly*
freshly ground black pepper

1 Preheat the grill and cook the bacon, then cool, slice and set aside. Preheat the oven to Gas Mark 6/200°C/fan oven 180°C.

2 Bring a saucepan of water to the boil and cook the pasta according to the packet instructions. Drain and return to the pan.

3 In a separate saucepan, bring the milk to the boil, add the fish and cook gently for 4–5 minutes. Remove with a slotted spoon and flake.

4 Strain the milk into a bowl and cool a little. Add the crème fraîche, eggs, mustard, cheese and bacon and season with pepper. Stir this into the pasta, along with the flaked fish.

5 Spoon into a 2 litre (3½ pint) ovenproof dish. Using a food processor or hand-held blender, whizz the bread to make breadcrumbs then arrange the tomato slices on top and sprinkle over the breadcrumbs. Bake for 20–25 minutes until the top is golden and the mixture is set.

Pork paprika

Pamela Lloyd from Leigh-on-Sea in Essex really looks forward to her weekly meeting run by Diane Davis. This recipe originally came from Pamela's husband and he regularly prepared this for her, ready for when she got home from work.

Serves 2
15 *ProPoints* values per recipe
15 minutes preparation, 1 hour 15 minutes cooking

½ tablespoon olive oil
1 onion, chopped
1 tablespoon paprika
4 tablespoons tomato purée
150 ml (5 fl oz) hot chicken stock
2 × 125 g (4½ oz) lean pork loin steaks
175 g (6 oz) button mushrooms
salt and freshly ground black pepper

1 Preheat the oven to Gas Mark 4/180°C/fan oven 160°C.

2 Heat the oil in a medium pan and cook the onion gently for around 10 minutes until softened. Stir in the paprika and cook for 30 seconds, then stir in the tomato purée.

3 Remove from the heat and stir in the stock then return to the heat and bring slowly to the boil, stirring well. Turn off the heat.

4 Tear off enough foil to make a parcel and place in a 2 litre (3½ pint) ovenproof dish. Put the pork steaks in the dish, season, spoon over the sauce and seal the parcel. Cook in the oven for 1 hour, until the meat is tender.

5 Open the parcel and add the mushrooms, then re-seal. Return to the oven for 15 minutes to cook the mushrooms and then serve.

Spicy vegetable satay stir-fry with noodles

Jo Brooker from Whitfield in Northamptonshire says her Leader Linda is an inspiration. This hearty and tasty meal has been a firm family favourite in the Brooker household for many years. Jo recommends varying the vegetables to suit your taste.

V Serves 2
16 *ProPoints* values per recipe
20 minutes in total

40 g (1½ oz) peanut butter
1 tablespoon soy sauce
1 tablespoon lemon juice
1 tablespoon mild curry powder
a kettleful of boiling water
80 g (3 oz) dried medium egg noodles
calorie controlled cooking spray
1 small onion, chopped finely
1 red pepper, de-seeded and diced
1 small courgette, diced
6 small mushrooms, sliced
1 garlic clove, chopped finely
1 red fresh chilli, de-seeded and chopped finely
1 tablespoon chopped fresh coriander, to garnish

1 Put the peanut butter in a measuring jug with the soy sauce, lemon juice and curry powder. Pour enough boiling water in the jug to measure 150 ml (5 fl oz). Stir to dissolve the peanut butter, then set aside.

2 Bring a saucepan of water to the boil and cook the noodles according to the packet instructions. Drain well.

3 Meanwhile, spray a non stick wok or large frying pan with the cooking spray and cook the onion, pepper, courgette, mushrooms, garlic and chilli over a high heat for around 5 minutes.

4 Add the peanut sauce to the pan with the drained noodles. Lower the heat and continue to cook for 2 minutes to heat everything through. Divide between two bowls and serve with the coriander sprinkled on top.

Beef casserole

Heather Simmons has been clerking at her meeting in Upper Killay, Swansea, for years and thinks her Leader Caroline Daniels is fantastic. This lovely casserole is a recipe that Heather's mum Amy used to make when she was a child. She adapted it and it became a firm family favourite. It's so good that her daughter now makes it for her own family.

Serves 4
43 *ProPoints* values per recipe
20 minutes preparation + soaking, 5 hours cooking

50 g (1¾ oz) dried pearl barley
100 g (3½ oz) dried haricot beans
100 g (3½ oz) dried butter beans
4 carrots, peeled and sliced
1 onion, sliced
250 g (9 oz) button mushrooms, cleaned
400 g (14 oz) lean braising steak, sliced
600 g (1 lb 5 oz) potatoes, such as Maris Piper, peeled and cut into 3–4 cm (1¼–1½ inch) chunks
4 fresh thyme or rosemary sprigs
1 litre beef stock
salt and freshly ground black pepper

1 Place the pearl barley and beans in a large bowl. Pour over 1 litre (1¾ pints) of cold water, cover and leave to soak overnight, or for at least 8 hours. Drain and rinse under fresh cold water.

2 Preheat the oven to Gas Mark 1/140°C/fan oven 120°C. Put the carrots, onion and mushrooms in a large 4 litre (7 pint) ovenproof casserole dish with a tight-fitting lid. Season, then top with the drained beans and barley, then the beef, and finally the potatoes, seasoning well between each layer. Add the herbs.

3 Pour the stock over the potatoes. If the potatoes are not completely covered with liquid, add more boiling water as required.

4 Cover and cook in the oven for 5 hours, until tender. Season to taste, then serve.

Spicy chicken livers

With the support of her Leader, Debbie, *Sue Keen* from Middlewich in Cheshire has lost two stone. She chose this recipe because it's low in *ProPoints* values, inexpensive and her husband loves it.

Serves 2
14 *ProPoints* values per recipe
40 minutes in total + marinating

100 g (3½ oz) chicken livers, cut into 1 cm (½ inch) thick slices
1 tablespoon balsamic vinegar
1 teaspoon olive oil
1 tablespoon finely chopped fresh coriander, plus extra to garnish
1 green fresh chilli, de-seeded and chopped finely
100 g (3½ oz) green beans, trimmed
75 g (2¾ oz) dried couscous
2 rashers lean back bacon, rind removed, and cut into 1 cm (½ inch) pieces
125 ml (4 fl oz) chicken stock
salt and freshly ground black pepper

1 Put the livers in a bowl with the vinegar, oil, coriander and chilli. Mix gently. Cover and marinate in the fridge for 30 minutes or up to 2 hours.

2 Meanwhile, bring a medium pan of water to the boil. Add the green beans, bring back to the boil and cook for 2 minutes until just tender. Drain and refresh under cold water. Cut into 2½ cm (1 inch) pieces.

3 To prepare the couscous, bring a lidded saucepan of 100 ml (3½ fl oz) water to the boil, remove from the heat and stir in the couscous. Cover and set aside for 5 minutes.

4 Meanwhile, drain the livers and keep the marinade. Heat a wok or large non stick frying pan over a high heat. Add the bacon and dry-fry for 2 minutes until beginning to colour. Add the livers and cook for 2 minutes, turning occasionally, until browned all over.

5 Add the reserved marinade, beans and stock to the pan, stirring well to scrape up any pieces from the base of the pan. Boil rapidly for 1–2 minutes until slightly reduced and thickened. Fluff up the warm couscous with a fork, season to taste and serve immediately, garnished with coriander.

Desserts

Banoffee toffee pie

Gold Member *Karen Shepherd* from Walton near Chesterfield has been a Weight Watchers Member for 30 years. She loves cooking and created this decadent dessert for those times when a fruit salad just isn't enough. Our judges thought it was simply stunning.

Serves 6
45 *ProPoints* values per recipe
30 minutes in total + chilling

calorie controlled cooking spray
120 g (4½ oz) digestive biscuits
1 egg white, beaten lightly
3 gelatine sheets, cut into small pieces
200 g (7 oz) Quark
100 g (3½ oz) low fat soft cheese
100 ml (3½ fl oz) light double cream, whipped
25 g (1 oz) icing sugar, sifted
100 g (3½ oz) ready-made toffee sauce
2 bananas
2 tablespoons lemon juice

1 Preheat the oven to Gas Mark 3/160°C/fan oven 140°C. Spray an 18 cm (7 inch) ovenproof flan dish with cooking spray.

2 Put the biscuits in a bowl and using the end of a rolling pin, crush into fine crumbs. Add the egg white and mix well to combine. Press the biscuit mixture into the base of the dish. Bake for 5–7 minutes until just firm.

3 Put the gelatine in a heatproof bowl and cover with cold water. Leave to soak for 5 minutes or until soft. Drain using a sieve. Return to the bowl and place over a pan of just simmering water. Heat for 2 minutes until melted, then remove from the heat and leave to cool slightly.

4 Beat the Quark and soft cheese together until smooth. Stir in the cream and icing sugar, combine and then add the cooled gelatine. Drizzle over half of the toffee sauce and fold in very briefly to swirl it through.

5 Slice one of the bananas and toss with half of the lemon juice. Spread out over the biscuit base then top with the cream mixture and level the surface. Cover and chill for at least 30 minutes or for up to 24 hours.

6 Slice the remaining banana and toss it with the remaining lemon juice. Arrange the slices over the pie. Drizzle over the remaining toffee sauce before serving.

Fruit crème brûlée

Sandra Mellor from Rhyl, Wales, says this yummy recipe is very quick and easy. Simply assemble then add the sugar and grill when you're ready to eat.

V Serves 4
24 *ProPoints* values per recipe
20 minutes in total

75 g (2¾ oz) amaretti biscuits
2 tablespoons crème de cassis
225 g (8 oz) strawberries, hulled and any large fruit halved or quartered
125 g (4½ oz) mixed summer berries, such as raspberries and blueberries
200 g (7 fl oz) Weight Watchers low fat crème fraîche
200 g (7 fl oz) 0% fat Greek yogurt
4 tablespoons light brown soft sugar

1 Preheat the grill to high. Put the amaretti biscuits in a 17 × 22 cm (6½ × 8½ inch) shallow ovenproof baking dish so they cover the base completely.

2 Drizzle over the crème de cassis and leave it to soak for 5 minutes. Scatter the fruit evenly over the top.

3 Mix the crème fraîche and yogurt together in a bowl and spoon over the fruit, smoothing the surface evenly.

4 Sprinkle the top with the sugar. Place under the grill for 2–3 minutes or until melted and caramelised. Remove from the grill and leave to rest for 2–3 minutes before serving.

Try this

Adjust the fruit according to what's in season, and vary the liqueur if you prefer – sherry and Marsala make tasty alternatives.

Apple and sultana crumble

Janette Mulqueen from Glasgow works in the community as an Enhanced Carer and says the flexibility of the *ProPoints* plan is ideal for her schedule. Enjoy this lovely crumble with 150 g (5½ oz) low fat custard for an additional 3 *ProPoints* values per serving or 1 tablespoon of 0% fat Greek yogurt per person for an additional 1 *ProPoints* value per serving.

V Serves 2
8 *ProPoints* values per recipe
15 minutes in total + cooling

2 cooking apples, peeled, cored and sliced
30 g (1¼ oz) sultanas
¼ teaspoon ground cinnamon
¼ teaspoon ground mixed spice
For the topping
30 g (1¼ oz) porridge oats
2 teaspoons demerara sugar
¼ teaspoon ground cinnamon
¼ teaspoon ground mixed spice
1 teaspoon vegetable (or other unflavoured) oil

1 Put the apple slices in a small saucepan and add the sultanas, cinnamon, mixed spice, and 2 tablespoons of cold water. Warm over a medium heat for 5 minutes, until the apples have softened. Remove from the heat and allow to cool. Divide the apple evenly between two glasses or dishes.

2 Next make the topping. Place all the topping ingredients in a non stick frying pan and cook for 2–3 minutes, stirring continuously until the oats are golden. Remove from the heat and allow to cool for 1–2 minutes.

3 Sprinkle the topping evenly over the apple and serve.

Cook's tips

This dessert is ideal for entertaining as you can make the two separate elements in advance and then assemble when needed.

When catering for more people, simply multiply the ingredients as required.

Spiced apple charlotte

Meeting helper *Sandra Nicholson*, from Kidlington, Oxfordshire, created this recipe as a compromise between her partner's love of apple crumble and her desire for a low *ProPoints* value dessert. Now there is something they can both enjoy.

V Serves 4

16 *ProPoints* values per recipe

15 minutes preparation, 30 minutes cooking

calorie controlled cooking spray
4 × 40 g (1½ oz) medium slices wholemeal bread
4 teaspoons low fat spread
275 ml (9½ fl oz) skimmed milk
2 Bramley cooking apples (500 g/1 lb 2 oz total)
4 heaped teaspoons granulated sweetener
1 teaspoon mixed spice
4 teaspoons demerara sugar

1 Preheat the oven to Gas Mark 5/190°C/fan oven 170°C. Spray an 18 × 22 cm (7 × 8½ inch) ovenproof baking dish with cooking spray. Spread each slice of bread with the spread and cut each slice into four triangles.

2 Put the milk in a shallow dish and lay the bread, spread-side up, into the milk. Set aside for 5 minutes until all the milk has been absorbed.

3 Meanwhile, peel, core and slice the apples. Put them in a bowl with the sweetener and mixed spice. Spread the fruit over the base of the prepared baking dish.

4 Arrange the bread slices, spread-side up, attractively over the top. Sprinkle with the demerara. Bake in the oven for about 25–30 minutes until the top is crisp and golden. Serve immediately.

Cook's tip

This recipe works well for any number of servings from 1 person upwards. Simply divide the ingredient quantities by four per serving. Adjust the size of the baking dish accordingly.

Easy summer pudding

Pat Furniaux from Chatham, Kent says this is a family favourite and it's so easy since it uses store cupboard ingredients. Her Leader, Kelly Wheatley, is helpful and supportive and all the Members in her meeting encourage each other to stay on track.

V Serves 6

10 *ProPoints* values per recipe

20 minutes in total + overnight chilling

500 g (1 lb 2 oz) pack frozen summer fruits
1 × 23 g pack sugar free raspberry or blackcurrant jelly
a kettleful of boiling water
7 × 40 g (1½ oz) medium slices white bread,
    crusts removed

1 Line a 1.2 litre (2 pint) pudding basin with cling film.

2 Put the frozen fruit in a medium size saucepan and warm over a medium heat for 5 minutes until defrosted and slightly softened. Remove from the heat.

3 Place the jelly into a measuring jug and add 250 ml (9 fl oz) of boiling water. Stir to dissolve, then add enough cold water to make it up to 600 ml (20 fl oz). Mix into the fruit and leave to cool slightly.

4 Spear a slice of bread with a fork and dip very briefly into the fruit and jelly liquid. Put into the bottom of the prepared basin. Repeat with the other slices one by one and line the sides of the basin, breaking or cutting the bread to fit if necessary and leaving enough bread for the top.

5 Spoon the fruit into the basin using a slotted spoon. Top with the remaining bread then very gradually pour over the jelly liquid until it is all absorbed. Cover and chill overnight. To serve, invert the pudding on to a plate. Remove the kitchen film and then cut into wedges to serve.

Serving suggestion

This is delicious with a 60 g (2 oz) scoop of low fat vanilla ice cream, for an additional 2 *ProPoints* values.

Peanut butter and banana bread pudding

Lisa Matusha from Thamesmead, London, loves cooking. This recipe came about when Lisa was making banana and peanut butter on toast. For only a few extra **ProPoints** values, she created this wonderful variation on a traditional bread and butter pudding.

V Serves 4

11 ProPoints values per recipe

10 minutes preparation, 30 minutes cooking

2 bananas, *cut into 1 cm (½ inch) slices*
30 g (1¼ oz) smooth or crunchy peanut butter
2 Weight Watchers slices thick wholemeal bread
1 egg
125 ml (4 fl oz) skimmed milk
1 teaspoon demerara sugar

1 Preheat the oven to Gas Mark 4/180°C/fan oven 160°C. Scatter the banana slices over the base of a small 15 × 20 cm (6 × 8 inch) shallow ovenproof baking dish.

2 Spread the peanut butter on the slices of bread and cut each slice into four triangles. Layer the bread, peanut butter-side up, attractively over the banana.

3 Whisk the egg and milk together and pour over the bread. Sprinkle the sugar over the top.

4 Bake in the oven for 25–30 minutes or until just firm. Remove from the oven. Leave to cool slightly before serving.

Serving suggestion

This is great served with 30 g (1¼ oz) Weight Watchers thick cream for an extra 1 **ProPoints** value per serving.

Cook's tip

If you're catering for more than four, this recipe can easily be multiplied.

Apple and blackberry sponge

Caroline Jones from Lydbrook, Gloucestershire, says that using fat-free sponge makes this a low **ProPoints** value pudding. You can use any fruit you like so it's ideal for anyone who enjoys fruit desserts.

V Serves 6

23 ProPoints values per recipe

20 minutes preparation, 40 minutes cooking

2 large cooking apples *(about 500 g/1 lb 2 oz)*
300 g (10½ oz) blackberries
2 tablespoons golden syrup
3 eggs
75 g (2¾ oz) caster sugar
75 g (2¾ oz) self-raising flour, sifted twice

1 Preheat the oven to Gas Mark 4/180°C/fan oven 160°C. Peel, core and dice the apples.

2 Spread the apple and blackberries out over the base of a 20 × 30 cm (8 × 12 inch) ovenproof baking dish and drizzle over the syrup. Bake in the oven for 20 minutes until starting to soften.

3 Meanwhile, put the eggs and sugar in a large heatproof bowl and whisk briefly to combine. Place the bowl over a pan of just simmering water, making sure the bowl doesn't touch the water. Using a hand-held electric whisk, whisk the mixture for 8–10 minutes, or until pale, thick and at least double the volume.

4 Remove the bowl from the heat and gently fold in the flour with a large metal spoon. Pour the mixture over the fruit, spreading it out quickly and evenly. Bake for 20 minutes or until well risen and golden. Serve hot or cold.

Fruit creates a luscious base for this dessert. Go ahead and try it with your favourites – rhubarb and plums are especially good but feel free to be adventurous.

cakes & **bakes**

Marshmallow and squash brownies

Jane Stuckey from Axminster in Devon always felt that 7 *ProPoints* values for a piece of chocolate cake was too high, so she created these deliciously sticky brownies to satisfy her chocolate cravings. They're lovely on their own or with 1 tablespoon of fat-free yogurt for an additional 1 *ProPoints* value per serving.

V Serves 25
89 *ProPoints* values per recipe
20 minutes preparation + cooling, 1 hour 45 minutes cooking

400 g (14 oz) butternut squash, *halved and de-seeded*
3 eggs
200 g (7 oz) light muscovado sugar
150 g (5½ oz) dark chocolate (minimum 70% cocoa solids), broken into pieces
100 g (3½ oz) ground almonds
2 teaspoons gram flour (gluten free and also known as 'besan' or chick pea flour)
1 teaspoon baking powder
1 teaspoon vanilla extract
200 g (7 oz) mini marshmallows

1 Preheat the oven to Gas Mark 4/180°C/fan oven 160°C. Line a 20 x 5 cm (8 x 2 inch) deep tin with baking parchment.

2 Put the squash on a baking sheet and bake in the oven for around 1 hour or until soft. Scoop the flesh out of the skin and into a bowl. Mash roughly, then leave to cool.

3 Using a hand-held electric whisk, whisk the eggs and sugar together in a large bowl for about 5 minutes until the mixture is pale and the whisks leave a ribbon-like trail.

4 Melt the chocolate in a bowl positioned over a saucepan of simmering water until melted or in a microwave, checking it every 30 seconds.

5 Add the squash, almonds, gram flour, baking powder and vanilla extract to the chocolate and mix well. Add this to the egg and sugar mixture and gently fold everything together. Stir in the marshmallows.

6 Spoon into the prepared tin and level. Bake for 35–45 minutes until the top is firm. Lift the cake, still in its paper, out of the tin. Cool on a wire rack. Cut into 25 pieces and store in an airtight container for up to 3 days.

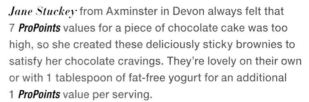

Banana and custard muffins

Lynn Bustard from Huntingdon, Cambridgeshire, has been a Gold Member for 16 years and is also a helper at her Hertford meeting. As she is retired now, she has more time to enjoy her hobby of cooking and makes this recipe regularly to use up leftover bananas. They are a real treat – a classic combination of delicious ingredients made into moist little cakes.

V ✳ Makes 12 muffins
43 *ProPoints* values per recipe
15 minutes preparation, 20 minutes cooking

100 g (3½ oz) low fat spread
150 g (5½ oz) light muscovado sugar
2 bananas, mashed
1 egg, beaten
3 tablespoons skimmed milk
100 g (3½ oz) self-raising flour
50 g (1¾ oz) custard powder
½ teaspoon baking powder

1 Preheat the oven to Gas Mark 4/180°C/fan oven 160°C. Line a 12 hole muffin tin with paper muffin cases.

2 Put the spread and sugar in a bowl and mix together until combined. Add the bananas, egg and skimmed milk and mix again.

3 Sift over the flour, custard powder and baking powder and fold everything together. Divide equally among the muffin cases, then bake for 20 minutes until the tops give slightly when pressed with a finger.

4 Lift out of the tin and cool on a wire rack.

Cook's tip
Store in an airtight container for up to 4 days or wrap and freeze for up to 3 months.

Camomile, honey and vanilla Swiss roll

Chris Dimmick from Lymington in Hampshire really values the support she gets from her Leader, Sue Pepper, and the other Members in her meeting – they share the successes and have plenty of laughs. This dessert has a deliciously unique flavour, thanks to an unusual ingredient – tea leaves. It's best eaten on the same day.

V Serves 10
34 *ProPoints* values per recipe
30 minutes in total + cooling

calorie controlled cooking spray
5 camomile, vanilla and honey herb tea bags
3 eggs
75 g (2¾ oz) caster sugar
75 g (2¾ oz) plain flour
1 teaspoon icing sugar
a few mint sprigs, to decorate
For the filling
100 ml (3½ fl oz) reduced fat double cream
25 g (1 oz) runny honey

1 Preheat the oven to Gas Mark 7/220°C/fan oven 200°C. Spray a 23 × 33 cm (9 × 13 inch) Swiss roll tin with the cooking spray then line with baking parchment.

2 Empty the filling of the tea bags into a large bowl. Add the eggs and caster sugar. Using a hand-held electric whisk, whisk for around 5 minutes on full speed until thick and mousse-like and the whisks leave a ribbon-like trail when lifted. Sift over the flour, then fold in gently with a metal spoon, taking care not to knock out too much air. Spoon into the prepared tin and bake for 8–10 minutes until well risen and the top feels springy.

3 Lay a warm and damp tea towel on the table and cover the towel with a sheet of greaseproof paper. Turn the Swiss roll out on to the greaseproof paper. Carefully peel away the baking parchment. Trim one crust off a short end of the cake, then roll up so the greaseproof sheet is lining it. Cool on a wire rack.

4 Whisk the cream and honey together in a bowl until thick and creamy. Unroll the Swiss roll, fill with cream and re-roll. Slide off the paper on to a plate. Sprinkle with icing sugar and decorate with mint sprigs. Serve immediately.

A delicately-flavoured and featherlight sponge is rolled up around a sweet cream filling to create a stunning tea time treat.

Orange fruit cake

Christine Faulder from Great Orton, Carlisle, says this fuss-free cake is perfect for when she wants something a little sweet. Once you've soaked the fruit, it only takes a few minutes to put together and tastes sublime. Christine recommends keeping this cake in the fridge so it stays fresher for longer.

V ❄ Serves 14

35 *ProPoints* values per recipe

15 minutes preparation + overnight soaking, 1 hour cooking

225 g (8 oz) mixed dried fruit
150 ml (5 fl oz) orange juice
110 g (4 oz) wholemeal self-raising flour
½ teaspoon mixed spice
1 teaspoon baking powder
40 g (1½ oz) low fat spread
1 egg, beaten

1 Put the dried fruit and orange juice in a bowl and set aside to soak overnight.

2 Preheat the oven to Gas Mark 2/150°C/fan oven 130°C. Line a 450 g (1 lb) loaf tin with baking parchment.

3 Sift the flour, mixed spice and baking powder into a large bowl. Add the spread and rub in with your fingertips until the mixture resembles breadcrumbs.

4 Stir the egg into the fruit mixture, then add this to the dry mixture. Mix everything together well until combined, then spoon into the prepared tin. Bake for 1 hour.

5 Remove from the oven and cool in the tin on a wire rack.

Cook's tip

Slice and store in an airtight container for up to 4 days, or slice and freeze for up to a month.

Carrot and walnut cake

Lynda Wills-Bantock from Solihull says her whole family enjoys this wholesome cake as it's light and fruity. Lynda recommends adding a butter cream topping (see Cook's tip) to this delicious cake for only a few additional *ProPoints* values.

V ❄ Makes 10 slices

45 *ProPoints* values per recipe

15 minutes preparation + cooling, 1½ hours cooking

calorie controlled cooking spray
200 g (7oz) wholemeal self-raising flour
½ teaspoon ground mixed spice
75 g (2¾ oz) low fat spread
100 g (3½ oz) light brown sugar
400 g (14 oz) carrots, grated
2 teaspoons raisins
2 teaspoons chopped walnuts
2 eggs, beaten
1 teaspoon runny honey, warmed

1 Preheat the oven to Gas Mark 4/180°C/fan oven 160°C. Line the base of a 900 g (2 lb) loaf tin with baking parchment and spray with cooking spray.

2 Sift the flour and mixed spice into a large bowl, adding the bran bits left in the sieve to the bowl. Add the spread and rub in with your fingertips until the mixture is well combined. Stir in the sugar.

3 Add the grated carrots, raisins, walnuts and the beaten eggs and mix together with a wooden spoon until all the flour has been absorbed into the mixture. Spoon into the tin, level the surface, and bake for 1–1½ hours or until a skewer comes out clean. Brush over the warm honey and leave to cool in the tin.

4 Once cool, remove from the tin.

Cook's tips

For a butter cream topping, mix together 50 g (1¾ oz) Weight Watchers crème fraîche, 20 g (¾ oz) low fat spread and 140 g (5 oz) icing sugar, for an extra 2 *ProPoints* values per slice.

Store, wrapped in cling film, for 3 days or slice and freeze for up to 3 months.

This wonderfully moist carrot cake is cleverly sweetened with carrots along with a few tasty raisins and some chopped walnuts. It's ideal for when friends stop by for a cup of tea.

Banana cake

This is a recipe that *Jenni Williams* from Newport used to make with her Nan as a child. Even though her Nan never weighed anything, her cakes always rose beautifully. Here is Jenni's version which is lower in *ProPoints* values and ideal for using up over-ripe bananas which give the best flavour.

V ❄ Makes 10 slices
49 *ProPoints* values per recipe
10 minutes preparation + cooling, 1¼ hours cooking

75 g (2¾ oz) low fat spread
75 g (2¾ oz) caster sugar
2 eggs, beaten
225 g (8 oz) self-raising flour
3 bananas, mashed to a pulp
75 g (2¾ oz) raisins

1 Preheat the oven to Gas Mark 4/180°C/fan oven 160°C. Line a 900 g (2 lb) loaf tin with greaseproof paper.

2 Beat the spread and caster sugar together in a bowl until pale and fluffy.

3 Gradually beat in the eggs until combined, then fold in the flour, bananas and raisins. Spoon into the prepared tin and bake for 1–1¼ hours until a skewer comes out clean.

4 Cool in the tin for 15 minutes, then take it out of the tin and leave to cool completely on a wire rack.

Cook's tip
Store in an airtight container for up to 4 days or wrap in cling film and freeze for up to 3 months.

Cherry and almond rock cakes

A Leader from Telscombe Cliffs, East Sussex, *Felicia Peters* joined Weight Watchers in 2000 and lost 8 stone; she has been at goal ever since. Felicia loves baking and adapts her favourite recipes to make them healthier. These bite-size treats are perfect for a mid-afternoon snack with a cup of tea. And the team at Weight Watchers loved them.

V ❄ Makes 30 cakes
54 *ProPoints* values per recipe
25 minutes in total + cooling

250 g (9 oz) self-raising flour
2 teaspoons baking powder
125 g (4½ oz) low fat spread
50 g (1¾ oz) light soft brown sugar
75 g (2¾ oz) glacé cherries, quartered
50 g (1¾ oz) currants
1 egg, beaten
3 tablespoons skimmed milk
2 teaspoons almond essence

1 Preheat the oven to Gas Mark 6/200°C/fan oven 180°C. Line two large baking sheets with baking parchment.

2 Sift the flour and baking powder into a large mixing bowl and rub in the spread until it resembles breadcrumbs.

3 Stir in the sugar, cherries and currants. Add the egg, milk and almond essence to make a slightly sticky dough.

4 Use a teaspoon to drop 30 blobs of the mixture on to the trays and bake for 10–12 minutes until risen and golden.

5 Transfer to a wire rack to cool.

Cook's tip
Store in an airtight container for up to 4 days.

Butternut squash rolls

Gold Member *Nicole Benjamin* from South Woodford, London, joined Weight Watchers after leaving university and went from a size 18 to a size 8. She loves bread and longed for a healthy bread recipe. Hearing that you could use butternut squash and very little sugar or fat to make rolls, she created this superb recipe.

V ✳ Makes 10 bread rolls

40 *ProPoints* values per recipe

20 minutes preparation + rising + cooling, 50 minutes cooking

400 g (14 oz) butternut squash, *peeled, de-seeded and chopped*
1 tablespoon olive oil
1½ teaspoons salt
1½ tablespoons sugar
350 g (12 oz) wholemeal flour,
*   plus extra for kneading*
7 g sachet fast action yeast
a pinch of grated nutmeg

1 Steam the squash in a pan for 20–30 minutes until tender. Put in a bowl and add the olive oil, salt, sugar and 4 tablespoons of cold water. Using a hand-held blender, whizz to make a purée.

2 Put the flour in a large bowl and stir in the yeast and nutmeg. Make a well in the middle and add the purée mixture. Stir all the ingredients together with a knife, then tip on to a board and knead for about 10 minutes until soft and sticky. Put into a clean bowl, cover and set aside in a warm place to rise for 1 hour.

3 Tip the dough on to a board and punch it down to knock it back. Divide into 10 equal pieces and shape each into a round. Line a tray with baking parchment and place each round on the tray. Leave to prove (rise) for 30 minutes. Meanwhile, preheat the oven to Gas Mark 4/180°C/fan oven 160°C.

4 Bake for 15–20 minutes until the rolls sound hollow when tapped underneath. Cool on a wire rack.

Cook's tip
Store in an airtight container for up to 4 days or wrap and freeze for up to 3 months.

ProPoints value index

Light meals, lunches and snacks

1 ProPoints value or less

Spicy Chinese soup 10

Spicy courgette and butternut squash soup 8

Spicy roasted tomato soup 13

Spinach, leek and mozzarella parcels 17

2 ProPoints values or less

Sausage savouries 14

Twice-baked smoked salmon soufflés 9

3 ProPoints values or less

Courgette and cheese soup 12

Quorn with beetroot salad 7

4 ProPoints values or less

Cauliflower gratin d'Avril 8

Stilton pâté and pears 16

5 ProPoints values or less

Low fat Scotch eggs 14

Potato cakes with feta 16

7 ProPoints values or less

Cambodian chicken salad 12

8 ProPoints values or less

Warm salad Niçoise with cod 10

Main meals

2 ProPoints values or less

Guilt-free ratatouille 46

4 ProPoints values or less

Sausage, apple and ginger casserole 48

Stuffed butternut squash with Quorn 41

Sweet honey and orange veggie bake 24

Turkey stroganoff 42

5 ProPoints values or less

Cod with pesto and cheese topping 47

6 ProPoints values or less

Curried chicken bake 34

Thai style chicken noodle broth 25

Thyme-scented pork with creamy green veg 54

7 ProPoints values or less

Pasta-less lasagne 44

Pork, turkey and chorizo burgers 31

Spicy chicken livers 58

Tray-baked plaice with spinach and olives 50

Vietnamese fish 24

8 ProPoints values or less

Bolognese burgers 38

Caribbean chicken 19

Pork paprika 56

Spanish chicken involtini 32

Spicy vegetable satay stir-fry with noodles 56

Vegetable chick pea balti 22

Venison sausage casserole 40

9 ProPoints values or less

Beef risotto 20

Cauliflower risotto 26

Lamb moussaka 30

Roast in a bag 36

Romanesque chicken 22

Tarragon chicken thighs 28

10 ProPoints values or less

Chorizo tagliatelle 34

Creamy chicken with three mustards 40

Creamy hazelnut pasta 52

Italian lamb 26

Jacqui's turkey curry 50

Smoked haddock and bacon pasta bake 54

Sri Lankan pineapple curry 28

Summer risotto with trout 38

Tortilla lasagne 36

Venison in red wine 42

11 ProPoints values or less

Beef casserole 58

Fish benachin 52

Prawn saganaki 48

12 ProPoints values or less

Creamy bacon pasta 32

Thai Quorn red curry 46

13 ProPoints values or less

Thai tuna 20

Desserts

2 ProPoints values or less

Easy summer pudding 64

3 ProPoints values or less

Peanut butter and banana bread pudding 66

4 ProPoints values or less

Apple and blackberry sponge 66

Apple and sultana crumble 62

Spiced apple charlotte 64

6 ProPoints values or less

Fruit crème brûlée 62

8 ProPoints values or less

Banoffee toffee pie 61

Cakes and bakes

2 ProPoints values or less

Cherry and almond rock cakes 74

3 ProPoints values or less

Camomile, honey and vanilla Swiss roll 70

Orange fruit cake 72

4 ProPoints values or less

Banana and custard muffins 70

Butternut squash rolls 76

Marshmallow and squash brownies 69

5 ProPoints values or less

Banana cake 74

Carrot and walnut cake 72